Goodbye Burma tells the
of a family caught up in a
Burma is bombed and over
World War Two.

It follows the fortunes of different family members as they join the hundreds of thousands of others who leave behind their lives and homes, many trekking out on treacherous routes through the mountains to the safety of India.

Drawing on her own family's documents and memories, and on much careful research, the author reimagines their experiences, as the various characters carry with them their personal dilemmas and preoccupations, their loves and losses.

Candid in its portrayal of the social divisions and administrative failures of the collapsing British raj, *Goodbye Burma* is both a warm-hearted, deeply human story and a powerful tale of end of empire.

Jean Ellis studied history at the London School of Economics, the School of Oriental and African Studies and Chennai University, writing her doctoral thesis on south Indian politics during the period between the two World Wars. She has worked for UK and international charities in South Asia, South-East Asia and Africa and has published two books on community development in Asian communities in the UK.

Recognising the value of individual stories to an understanding of social history, she offers assistance to people wanting to write up their life experiences:

www.write-memoirs.com

She has one son, a professional musician, and now lives in Kent.

GOODBYE BURMA

Jean Ellis

CHARLCOMBE BOOKS

Charlcombe Books
17 George's Road, Bath BA1 6EY
Tel 01225-335813

First published 2017

ISBN 978 0 9568510 9 3

Printed and bound in Great Britain by
CPI Antony Rowe, Bumpers Way, Chippenham SN14 6LH

For Mark and Daniel,

and for Hazel, my link to Burma

CONTENTS

'We had so many visitors and wonderful parties,' Jo-Jo told me. Somerset Maugham stayed in the 1920s, she said, when Fran and Mouse were still young, and he was already a well-known writer. And Lion, it seemed, knew everyone, from Orwell himself to the royal princesses. There was even a story of how her father, Robert, had been taken to the royal palace at Mandalay as a baby, a few years before King Thibaw's exile to India, and been given a magnificent ruby and a solid golden bowl as presents.

'What happened to them – the presents?' I asked.

'Lost, with everything else. Lost . . .'

Author's note

This book is based on real events. It is the story of my mother's family, who left their home and everything they had when World War II came to Burma at the end of 1941. It tracks events as the Japanese did the inconceivable – invaded the country from the south, bombed Rangoon and pushed the British forces into Upper Burma. Hundreds of thousands of civilians evacuated – at first, those who could by sea and plane; then crowding onto the roads and into insanitary refugee camps. They walked out on treacherous routes: through the Taungup Pass in Arakan, through the Kabaw Valley and across the mountains into Manipur in India, or finally were pushed further north and across the notorious Hukawng Valley where they suffered starvation and disease, trekking through the jungles in the monsoon rains. Many thousands perished on the way.

The evacuation from Burma in 1942 was a tragic episode shaped by strategic decisions and administrative failings. Those with influence and money, mainly the British and other Europeans, got their families out first, leaving the Indians, Anglo-Indians and Anglo-Burmese, who were part of the economic fabric of the British empire in Burma, and on whom the administration relied for its essential services, to scramble out as best they could. It's a story that, particularly over the last few years, has begun to be told, both through historical accounts and through memoir.

I wanted to tell my own family's story – one that's specific in its detail but that will have parallels in the stories of many others. I began writing this book many years ago, when I was given a cousin's diary, started when Singapore fell in February 1942. I put my cousin's diary together with an account of those months as told to me by my uncle who, as a young man, served with the newly-formed Burma Army Signals. Finally, I wanted to tell the story of another cousin, one of many women who crossed the mountains on foot into Manipur in groups, until the route was blocked off for the military retreat. The diary that runs through the book is my cousin's diary, heavily edited, but essentially as it was written. The rest is what happened, but reimagined; the characters and the details of their lives may often resemble those of real people, but they have been created for this story. Their names are not those of my family or their friends. However, the names of officials that they meet along the way remain unchanged.

I have retained the names of towns, roads and lakes as they were known in 1942 and with the spelling used in my cousin's diary. Many of these names or their official spelling have since changed.. The Family lived on the north side of Inya Lake in Yangon (then Lake Victoria). This area was then known as Kokine, although now only the south side of Inya Lake is recognised as such.

I have tried to be historically credible wherever possible. The India Office Records in the British Library were enormously useful, as were the diaries and other personal accounts of those months. I was also helped by a number of published books that have told the story of these six months in Burmese and British colonial history. My aunt was thirteen when she left Rangoon and her memories were also invaluable, both in their detail and in firing my imagination.

Jean Ellis
September 2017

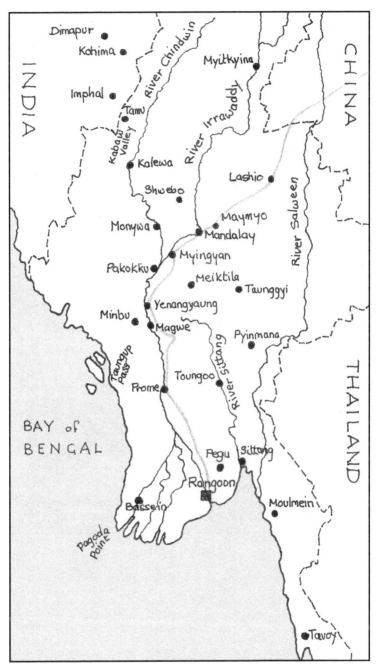

Map of Burma

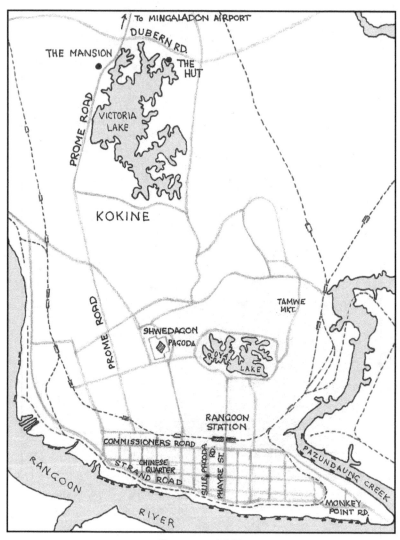

Rangoon 1942

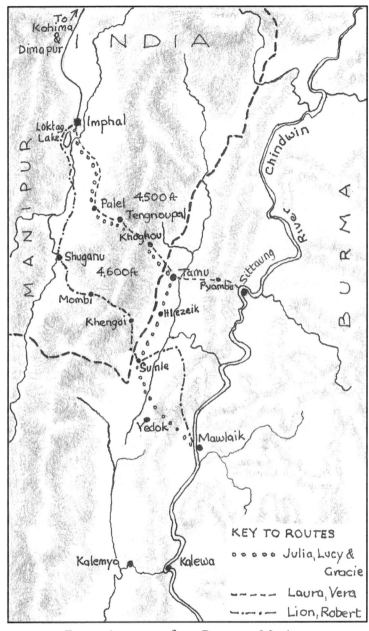

Evacuation routes from Burma to Manipur

CAST OF CHARACTERS

Stapleton family, London and Rangoon
Chrissie Stapleton, a teacher
Bobby Stapleton, her father, Liaison Officer, Burma Army Signals
Robert Stapleton, father of Bobby, Marcie and Joyce (Jo-Jo),
    fire insurance assessor
Louisa Stapleton, Robert's sister, matriarch of the Stapleton household
Lionel Hennessey (Lion), Bobby's cousin, District and Sessions Judge
Fran Hennessey, Bobby's cousin
Mouse Hennessey, Bobby's cousin
Laura Ferguson, Bobby's cousin
Appaswamy, the Stapleton family's butler

Other family members, Rangoon
Harry Ferguson, Laura's husband,
    manager in the Irrawaddy Flotilla Company
Bea, Bobby's aunt; Robert's sister-in-law
Lester, Bea's husband, District and Sessions Judge
Babs, Bea's sister
Issie, Bea's daughter

Other characters, Bobby's story
Ismail, Bobby's orderly
Frank Hurlings, member of the yacht club
Paul Lamont, retired timber merchant
Daw Min Min, his wife
Eva Lamont, his daughter
Doris Godfrey, acquaintance of Bobby
Ba Yee, Robert's handyman
Butler, a sergeant-major at HQ

Other characters, Laura's story
Vera Langham, friend of Laura
Peter Langham, her husband
Tommy and Ben, the Langham children
Bertha Smith, a friend of Vera
Dick Smith, her husband, a friend of Bobby
Kureeya, Dick Smith's servant
Julia Steele, a nurse
Gracie Shaw, Julia's friend; Bertha Smith's cousin
Tim Shaw, her husband

Lucy, Gracie's friend
Jabira Manzoor, a fellow trekker
Rabia and Jehan, Jabira's children
Hussein, an employee of Jabira Manzoor's husband

Other characters, Lion's story
Murthi, Lion's servant/bearer, Pegu and throughout

Mandalay
U Tun Tin, Assistant Secretary to the Senate
EL Manley, Deputy Commissioner of the Railways
Gledhill, District and Sessions Judge
Hendriks, District and Sessions Judge
CB De Kretzer, District Judge
Mr and Mrs Ghose, Lion's creditors
U Hla Pe, Lion's creditor
U Ba U, lawyer with the High Court, Rangoon
WH Payton, Chief Secretary to the Government
Lascelles, acquaintance of Lion's, evacuated to Mandalay
Vertannes, proprietor, Globe Welding Works

Maymyo
Gerald Bourne, lawyer, appointed Food Officer in Maymyo
HF Dunkley, Chief Justice, Maymyo
Thomas Healy, war correspondent, Daily Mirror
Weymss, official in the Home Secretary's office, Maymyo
Sir Paw Tun, Burmese Premier

Magwe
BW Swithenbank, Commissioner, Magwe
A McCracken, First Secretary

Minbu
U Po Kha, Assistant Judge, Minbu

On the trek
Lt-Colonel GH Fraser
GD Stewart, Deputy Commissioner, Mawlaik
Dillon, brother of a district officer
Singh brothers, traders
U Pha Htaw, Assistant Judge, Monywa
U Tin Tut, Second Secretary, Evacuation Officer, Kalewa
Sutherland, Evacuation Officer, Mawlaik
Acheson, Evacuation Officer, Mawlaik

THE STAPLETON FAMILY TREE

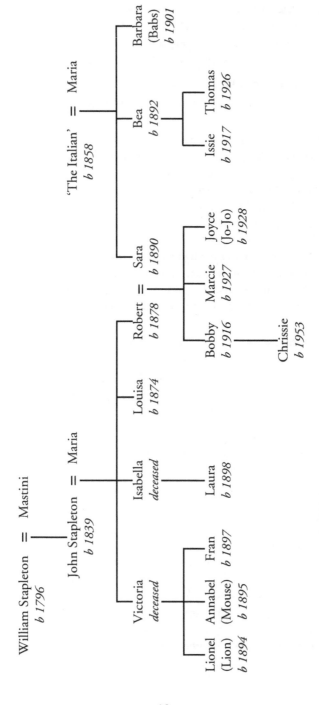

William Stapleton = Mastini
b 1796

John Stapleton = Maria
b 1839

'The Italian' = Maria
b 1858

Victoria
deceased

Isabella
deceased

Louisa
b 1874

Robert
b 1878

Sara
b 1890

Bea
b 1892

Barbara
(Babs)
b 1901

Lionel
(Lion)
b 1894

Annabel
(Mouse)
b 1895

Fran
b 1897

Laura
b 1898

Robert = Sara
b 1878   b 1890

Bobby
b 1916

Marcie
b 1927

Joyce
(Jo-Jo)
b 1928

Chrissie
b 1953

Issie
b 1917

Thomas
b 1926

18

1

CHRISSIE

October to December 1985

I got the call that Laura had died in October 1985. Towards the end of the month I stood in a south London crematorium with members of my dwindling family. It was an open, bleak space, flat against the skyline, broken only by some post-war tower blocks. There were other mourners, huddled and talking quietly together – other lives and losses we knew nothing about. Ours was the smallest group, swollen by some of the staff from the nursing home. My aunt Joyce – Jo-Jo – was smartly dressed as usual, her dark hair smooth and thick, brushed back from her finely-drawn brow and the line of her cheek, but her face was puffy from crying. Richard, her husband, grasped her by the elbow. Then my father, silent, seeming to be hardly present, content to allow others to manage the affair, I thought. I put my arm loosely through his, but it was an unfamiliar gesture and I soon pulled it away. I noticed the top of his head, as if someone had polished it a light mahogany, and the softness of his face and his lips. I felt sad for Laura, or a sort of nostalgia – for the young life she had in Burma before the war, long before I had known her – and in some ways grieving for the already fading memories of my own past.

I stayed only briefly at Jo-Jo's later, anxious to get home. As I kissed her goodbye, she said, 'Darling, come down in a week or two. Give me a ring, because I've got to sort out a few things of Laura's to give you.'

*

I had always known about Burma – the beautiful house at Monkey Point in Rangoon looking out onto the river, the rice mill my great-aunt Louisa had owned and the house in Kokine, with the lawns that ran down to the Victoria Lakes. I knew

19

that my family had lost it all in 1942 as the war advanced in the Pacific and the Japanese invaded Burma. I knew that my father, Bobby, had been with the retreating army, but he had never talked to me about those years and I hadn't asked him to tell me.

The family (the 'Family' we called them, with a capital F, as if they had a single, collective identity) settled in England after spending the rest of the war in India. In my early twenties, as the mid-1970s pushed away more heady student days, I had stayed with them for a while in their south London home, to save on rent and catch up on my university debts. By then the Family was reduced to a small group of elderly cousins: Laura, Fran and Mouse.

Sometimes I would stay in and watch television with them in the half-light of the lugubrious sitting room, reflections from the screen flickering on the glass doors of the darkened conservatory. The women seemed cut off inside their old Victorian house, the daily routine only occasionally broken by a visit from one of the old Burma crowd; it seemed as if they lived in the modern world by proxy, through the television and the occasional visitor.

Mouse and Fran were sisters, like two halves of the same story – one short and plump, the other tall and elegant, both bespectacled, intelligent, eager, one rarely starting a conversation without the other one joining her, elaborating, completing sentences. There was a quietness about them. Laura, their cousin, had a different sort of energy. She'd grown stout over the years but her face, always freshly powdered, was still young and good-humoured. She wore silk blouses that buttoned over to one side, with little mandarin collars and loose-fitting sleeves. On those television evenings in the sitting room, she was rarely without a notepad on her knee, copying out in her neat hand the translations of Chinese poetry that her cousin, Lionel, had done years before.

Lionel had died some years earlier; he had been something of a philosopher and a Chinese scholar, fluent in Mandarin. Lion, as the Family called him, had also been a passionate collector of books. They were still stacked in their faded leather binding in the heavy oak and glass-fronted bookcases that lined the sitting room. The walls were hung with old prints of pagodas and *sampans* floating on misty rivers. A colourful Chinese statue of the Buddha dominated the sideboard.

*

I went back to Jo-Jo's a few weeks after the funeral and spent half an hour sorting through old button boxes, silver buckles and bracelets with dragons' heads, rows of little ivory elephants and a print of a large pagoda, inscribed on the back in faded ink, *Rangoon, Shwedagon Pagoda*.

Before I left, Jo-Jo said, 'Oh, wait, Chrissie. Laura left boxes of papers and things that Richard has sorted out. He had to throw an awful lot away, but we kept a box which we thought you might like to look through.'

Richard produced a large cardboard box filled with leather-bound books and various other papers. I lifted a few out.

'They seem to be mainly newspaper cuttings, but I'll take a look at them.' I felt quite excited and we piled the box and the few mementos into the back of my old Renault.

When I got home I opened a bottle of wine and pulled the various volumes and folders out of the box, sifting through them on my knees. The large volumes were scrapbooks filled with wartime cuttings, most collected while the Family were in India in the mid-1940s. The leather-bound volumes were a disappointment, two of them containing lists of household effects, probably goods shipped out from Burma or from India later on. Then there were small notebooks, Lion's diaries of life in London in the 1950s. But they didn't contain much, recording meetings and titles of books, written in a mixture of thin, almost indecipherable writing and shorthand, which I couldn't read at all.

I was disappointed and left the rest of the folders, picking them up again the following evening with little expectation. They contained poetry, translations and Lion's own verses, turgid in style and of no real interest and then, in a little bundle, some thin, folded papers and three photos. Two photos were of the deck of a steamer, packed with people, labelled on the back: 'Evacuees on the Irrawaddy River', and there was one of a group of people walking along a jungle track, inscribed 'Trek'.

The folded papers proved to be mainly letters and I saw that they were from my grandfather, Robert, written in early 1942. I quickly read through one of them.

Rangoon
31 January 1942

My darling girls,

I hope you are taking care of yourselves. You cannot imagine how relieved we are to hear that Louisa and Fran had arrived safely in Calcutta when their telegram arrived yesterday, and to have news of you both. We had heard that a Japanese submarine had sunk two boats in the Bay and we were terribly anxious.

The house seems very quiet now that the pair of you are no longer here to worry me. Have you spent all your pocket money? You must miss the Lake, the swims and the outings in the boats. Well, this exile won't last long because I'm certain that we shall eventually drive the Japs out of Burma.

Fran will have given you all the news up until they left. Since then we have had quite a few alerts but, despite their efforts, the Japs have not been able to come over Rangoon.

Bobby has shifted to Aunt Bea's place because they are going to Kalaw or Maymyo in a day or two. But I'm going to stick it out in Kokine. I cannot concentrate on anything nowadays on account of the continual alerts. The siren is just opposite my office and it makes such an infernal and weird noise that the sound, combined with the noise of the cars and lorries as they skedaddle out of town, is enough to upset one from settling down to steady work.

Please don't worry about Bobby, Lion or myself. We are all quite all right, and if things come to the worst, we may have to trek out. I shall escort Lion to safety and our jungle experience will come in handy. Bobby of course will be the first to leave if the military decide to evacuate.

I'm glad to hear that you miss me, Marcie. I told you often you would once I am no longer near you.

Tons of love and a tight hug for both of you.

Your loving,

Dad

There was another letter to Marcie and Jo-Jo, and several written to Louisa and Fran, giving them details of remittances and news about the increasing air of panic in Rangoon as the Japanese forces moved up through Lower Burma. By February, Robert was reporting increasing disturbance from air alerts and dog fights over the city. It seemed that Rangoon was abuzz with talk of overland routes to India.

I wanted to find out more. And who was Aunt Bea?

*

I was having lunch with my father the following Sunday and decided to take the letters with me. He had lived alone since my mother left him several years before, moving to a small village in Hertfordshire. Every few weeks I made the dreary drive out through north London to spend a few hours with him.

The small living room of the cottage was already in half-light when we settled into its battered armchairs that winter afternoon with our cups of tea. I had mentioned the letters to Bobby over lunch, feeling awkward that I held something of his own father's that he hadn't seen, as though I were holding a tiny portion of his life. He'd looked up, seeming slightly confused.

'Letters from Daddy? I didn't know there were any. Well . . . I'll read them later.'

Setting my cup down on a side table, I took the letters out and suggested that he have a look at them.

'I would really like to hear what you remember about those times, Dad. Now that Laura's died I feel that you're the only one with the history.'

'I'll see how I can help, darling, but I don't know that I can remember a lot. It was a painful time and I don't like to think about it.'

He took his glasses out of his breast pocket and put them half-way on his nose, then reached out for the letters. He held them folded for a moment, and then spoke in his soft voice.

'The Stapletons had been in Burma for a long time and, you know, there was even a road named after us – Stapleton Road. At one time the Family had a beautiful house there, and a business also – very successful. We always went to the cemetery after church to put flowers on the family tomb, so it was really an upset to leave Burma the way we did. It was a very green country, very beautiful . . .'

He cleared his throat and started reading the letters, shaking his head and exclaiming from time to time as he turned over the pages.

'Now, the letters are from my father to my sisters. You see, the girls went across to India by boat, quite early on, with Mouse. Huh! I'd forgotten that Mouse went with them.'

I could see that doors were opening gently and, to his surprise, easily on memories which had long been shut away. As my father began talking, I was trying to sort out in my head the timing of events and started a question, but he was already deep into things that happened more than forty years before.

'People were moving north, retreating into Upper Burma all the time as the Japanese came. The civilian population became refugees just like that and they were all coming through with everything they had on their backs or on their heads. If they could get transport, they grabbed it. Otherwise they had to go by foot, you see.'

His voice became less reflective, almost passionate. 'You could see women carrying their little children – whole families – and sometimes they even took their pets with them; they didn't want to leave them behind. There were bullock carts with household belongings, although they were often abandoned later on at the side of the road, and cars too sometimes when they broke down. And those columns of people, and the evacuation camps that were set up for them, were targets for the Japanese bombers, you see. So a lot of them died on the way. Sitting ducks. Terrible.' He paused and then said, 'Anyway, as time went on, the panic increased. Everyone was rushing out and sometimes even families wouldn't wait for each other.'

The words hung there in the air for a while. The light was beginning to fade in the cottage, so I got up to put on a table lamp and then sat down again.

My father shifted around, looked up, stared at his left hand, rubbing his rounded finger tips with his thumb, then continued.

'Everyone was trying their best to get as much food as possible so that they could take it out with them. Cars were going which weren't even fit to do the journey and the whole route going south to north was just chaotic, so I was quite pleased to be on my own. I was a liaison officer with the Burma Army Signals, keeping the army in touch with the Telegraph office, so you see I was stuck with the army, and once the flap really started it was difficult to keep track of the Family, or what was left of them.'

He was quiet for a moment, then carried on, 'You see, Chrissie, until you showed me those letters, I hadn't thought . . . in all those years. And my sister, Marcie, we lost touch with her after the war. I don't know what happened to her. She met an American, some journalist fellow, and I believe she married him and went to live over there.'

Whenever my father was anxious, his face opened out. If there was a frown, it was momentary, a fleeting thing, pushed aside by lifted eyebrows, wide-open eyes. He turned to me now with that familiar, somewhat surprised expression.

'So many of us were scattered like that. People just disappeared and you didn't know if they were safe or not. Before the bombings, the events in the West hardly affected us at all. It all seemed two-dimensional, if you see what I mean. For most people life went on just the same as ever, with a certain amount of work, not very strenuous, you know, and in the evenings people played tennis and bridge, and the men drank in the clubs. Of course, we read accounts of the war that was going on, but it was as if we were spectators to something happening elsewhere. Then, gradually, little inconveniences began to make themselves felt: the post became irregular; the price of drink went up, so people noticed that! But I had to move around a lot and I was quite happy in that way. Because I was doing my bit, you see.'

He pushed himself out of his chair suddenly, cup in hand, moving towards the kitchen, leaving me still thinking about the tennis and the evenings spent in the club, and the leaving of it all.

*

When I got home that evening, exhausted from the drive through London's northern fringes, I poured a glass of wine and pulled the box of papers onto the floor in front of me, leafing carefully through the folders of cuttings and typescripts of talks that Lion had given in his early days in London during the 1950s. Then, looking inside an envelope, which at first seemed empty, I pulled out a single piece of paper. It was a poem, signed with my cousin Lion's name, LB Hennessey.

Burma

Infinite is the land's variety;
many the ways of her enchantment;
she laid a spell on me.

Over gold rice-fields the long v'd homing flight
of paddy-birds, curd white against a
grey cloud-fringe of the night.

In *padouk* time the fragrance everywhere,
a cool, damp rain – preluding breezes
from boughs bloom-heavy bear.

*

In the weeks that ran up to Christmas, I made several trips out to my father's cottage and, slowly, my father began the story of how he left Burma and how many of his friends didn't manage to get away, or died in the attempt.

2

BOBBY

December 1941

I wasn't on official leave over Christmas 1941, but I was hoping to spend time with the Family before I was due to head out of town again. Two days before Christmas Day, I turned off the Sule Pagoda Road just before ten o'clock and was driving towards headquarters to check in and pick up Ismail, my orderly, when the sirens went up. My reaction was one of disbelief and my immediate thoughts were to carry on to HQ and find out what was happening. It was impossible. The streets were crowded with people hurrying into work or shopping, and the road was now an affray, with rickshaws and bullock carts pulling in all directions. I tried to edge the car forward, but it became increasingly difficult. When the siren went off for a third time, other drivers abandoned their vehicles and ran to the sides of the road. A man in a white drill suit jumped out of a Ford some twenty yards ahead and gestured to me. The noise of the shouting above the warning siren added to the sense of unreality. Only minutes later, the terrible wail was replaced by a faint throb and then, overhead, the unmistakable drone of enemy aircraft. Jamming the brakes on, I jumped out of the jeep and crouched against the front wheel.

That was the first dog fight over the city, and it shattered the peace of mind of everyone in Rangoon, from government servants to rickshawallahs and dock labourers. It was very frightening that first time, watching the enemy planes coming into view, hearing the bombs whistling through the air and, as if in answer, the noise of anti-aircraft guns. The explosions sounded as though they were nearby and were almost deafening, but I could see vast plumes of grey smoke and hear a more distant thud of impact, and tumbling masonry as the bombs fell away to the other side of the city, in east Rangoon. As the bombers came closer, there was an overwhelming sense of panic in the street as people cried out to each other. It was almost as frightening as the sound of the bombs falling, but I kept my eyes fixed on the planes swooping downwards and the drama overhead.

As the all-clear sounded, my thoughts shifted suddenly to my father; he would be in his offices in Phayre Street. At the same time, as if with one movement, the street sprang back into action with a cacophony of sounds. A *gharry* swung round nearby, blocking a taxi that had stopped next to me. The driver, a large-jowled man, leant forward and swore loudly. I could see the sweat pouring down his cheeks; then his voice was drowned by the horns, which by now had set up a non-stop noise.

When I hit Strand Road, taking the route that led towards the docks, I was met by a scene of utmost chaos. People were rushing in all directions and there were dead and wounded lying where they had been struck by sticks of fragmentation bombs. Others were crying or calling out as they tried to escape from the scene, some carrying large loads on their heads, knees bent out in a desperate attempt to run. Even large children were snatched up and were being carried on backs and hips. A couple of ambulances arrived, attempting to make their way through. It would have been foolish for me to try to drive any further, so I decided to back up and head for the centre. It seemed that Phayre Street hadn't been directly hit and there was no reason to think that my father wouldn't be all right if he had been inside the office building.

At headquarters I was immediately struck by a new atmosphere. Things were hotting up. Later, I found Ismail in the dump. He had been working on one of the jeeps when the bombers came over and was making ready to return to the job when I arrived. I felt curiously comforted to find him, tools in hand, as though the reality of earlier that morning, before the bombers came over, still held good. We would still get our orders and perhaps tomorrow, or the day after that, we would be back on the road again. Ismail had been my orderly since I was commissioned the year before. Being on the road together so much, we had got used to each other's company. He was a good sort. He flashed a smile at me.

'I was worried about you, sahib. You have come through the centre of town, isn't it? They are saying that over the other side there are thousands killed.'

His mouth stretched across large gums and a prominent set of teeth, so that even in repose he tended to have a drawn, worried look, although he was a calm and cheerful enough bloke. But he looked disturbed now.

'I'm going to drive out to Kokine,' I said, 'but I won't be more than a couple of hours.' For a while I'd forgotten that Ismail's home was over by the docks, right in the path of the heaviest bombardment. 'I'll drive myself,' I said quickly. 'You check on your own family while I'm away.'

Thank goodness the two girls, Marcie and Jo-Jo, had got out when they had. There would be a hell of a panic now. My youngest sister, Jo-Jo, who was thirteen, had kicked up a terrible fuss and cried for days, although many of her school friends were also leaving. But my father had been adamant, and they had left by boat for Calcutta only two weeks previously.

During the seven miles to Kokine, the road was beginning to clog with vehicles and with people on foot moving away from the city, with hastily gathered possessions piled high on heads and in carts of every description. My mind was churning with thoughts about how we could clear up the house quickly so that the other women could leave as well. My aunt Louisa, my father's sister, had already agreed that she and my cousin Fran would join the girls in Calcutta as soon as she could book a passage, but my cousin Laura had a stubborn streak. After the girls left, she and her husband moved back from her own bungalow, joining my father in the Hut – our nickname for the family house. She wasn't making immediate plans to go. 'Let's wait and see,' Laura said.

I crossed the creek, sweeping round the hairpin bend which cut across the far end of the Victoria Lakes, taking in, as I always did, the peaceful view of the lakes at Kokine. I passed Laura's bungalow as I turned off the Prome Road and onto Dubern

Road, the red dust clouding out behind me. The garden was newly clipped and empty, and the house shuttered down.

I would no doubt find Laura at the Hut. The afternoon sun always hit you as you drove along the Dubern Road. Today, as usual, all was quiet as I passed the old family houses, set back in the open countryside. Then, coming to the village, just before the turn-off, I could see that I was deceived: this afternoon was different. The village was one long street, the flimsy, raised huts with their thatched roofs lining both sides. There was an unusual clamour and a movement of hand carts and rickshaws, giving an impression of continuous motion; the villagers had been joined by crowds coming out from the city.

I turned the jeep off the main road and drove rapidly into the long driveway which curved down to our house. I knew that Kokine had been untouched by the bombing, but I was anxious to have news and to reassure the family. Near the great banyan tree, the *mali* was cropping the grass with a sickle, bare-chested, his *dhoti* tucked up high. The Hut and the adjoining bungalow that Lion had built, overlooking the lake, breathed stillness. Siamese twins, Fran called the two bungalows, with their covered walkway between them.

Ba Yee, our handyman, was walking up to the house, his bright check *longyi* vivid against the white portico. He turned towards me, hearing the wheels skid slightly on the gravel. I waved to him and he disappeared inside. While I parked the jeep, I could hear from the kitchens the nasal tones of the cook, and a scraping and clattering of pots. Everyday noises. Aunt Louisa was expecting my arrival and came out to meet me before I reached the door. She was always a commanding figure – good-looking – with a strange contradiction between her grey hair, unaffectedly drawn into a net at the back, her neat lace collars, and the heavy jewellery on her slim wrists and fingers. She would sometimes lose her temper dreadfully, and her face was now set hard.

'It's terrible in town, Aunt Louisa, terrible. I've come to see how you all are.'

31

'It's not us,' she responded as we went in. 'They're not going to touch us out here.' And yet she was being forced to leave her home. My aunt was angry.

She gave a slight snort. 'Have you seen Robert?'

'Not yet, but he'll be fine.'

I went to find my cousins. Fran came quietly over to kiss me.

'Darling, we didn't hear you come in. We were busy getting back to all the preparations for Christmas. We have to keep going, don't we . . . not let it get to us? Oh, Bobby, we're so pleased to see you. We had no idea where you were this morning.'

Fran had tears in her eyes and I stepped over to give her a hug. Then, seeing Laura tight-lipped, for the first time that day I remembered her husband, Harry. I hurriedly reported the scene in Strand Road and Phayre Street. Harry worked for the Irrawaddy Flotilla Company; although he usually travelled a lot up-country, he must have been in the head office in Phayre Street when the bombers came over. I quickly reassured her.

'We could see the planes coming in, you know,' Laura said, but then we all went down to the trenches, except for Aunt Louisa. She refused; we couldn't make her come.'

'That doesn't surprise me.'

There had been air alerts since the middle of the month and we'd dug three large trenches. The ARP, in charge of air raid precautions, was persuading people of the need to use them when they heard the warning sirens.

Laura spoke quickly, almost stumbling over the words. 'We could hear the explosions from here. It was terrifying because we couldn't see what was going on.'

My cousin was a strong, intelligent woman who had married to get her independence from the Family. I reached out and touched her arm briefly.

'It was shocking . . . shocking,' I said. 'And there were some unlucky people out and about in Phayre Street, Laura, who were caught out. But, you will see, Harry would have kept safe after the sirens went up.'

'There must have been an awful lot of casualties over there. We could see it, Bobby. The servants are in a dreadful state about it, poor things. They don't know which areas are hit, but they are all worried for their neighbourhoods and their families.' Laura's voice dropped.

'Why don't I take Ba Yee back with me when I go?' I said, trying to keep the mood upbeat. 'Then he can report on things to you. I can't stay very long now, but I'll get back this evening if I can.'

I looked at the two women with a sudden rush of affection. I loved Fran. There was an elegance about her, although she no longer went out to the society parties she once loved. That afternoon, on the day of the first bombing of Rangoon, she was wearing tailored slacks, with some sort of striking blouse, an enamelled brooch at her neck. In her mid-forties, her hair was beginning to grey at the sides, but she still carried with her an aura of the flapper era. When she smiled, her face became brilliant, alive, leaving an edge of sadness around the mouth as the smile faded. Today I could see the anxiety etched on her face, her mouth drawn in sharply. Laura was a few years younger than her cousin. She had an infectious sense of humour and, before she was married, her laugh would often ring out loudly around the Hut. We were said to look alike, with the same low-bridged nose, both with a tendency to plumpness in the face.

Laura wrote out a telegram for me to send to Lion in Pegu, to the north-east of Rangoon. Lion had been appointed to Pegu as a sessions and circuit judge at the beginning of 1941. He was positioned right on the north-south Burma Road and was more in the line of the Japanese advance than we were in the city. But no one had expected the air attack on Rangoon; he would be anxious to have word of us. It would be chaos in the Post Office. Already there was talk of stacks of undelivered mail, the system breaking down beneath the volume of extra remittances, telegrams and the general burden of wartime.

*

I made my way back to Rangoon, Ba Yee beside me, unusually silent, occasionally pushing his hand through his oiled hair. Tamwe market was not far from the Pazundaung Creek, and it was in a terrible state after the morning's raid. I dropped Ba Yee nearby and then, back at headquarters, I was given orders to proceed to Pegu early the following morning. For now, I was free to return to the Hut and drove towards the railway station with Ismail. The movement of people out of Rangoon, which had already started when I was on the road earlier, had now become a flood. It was an alarming sight.

'They are all going, sahib; they are too frightened. The government has been telling them to stay put, but no one wants to die! I am thinking my family also should go.' Ismail sucked on his teeth.

It seemed as if half the population of Rangoon were trying to leave, with their bedrolls and belongings on their backs or heads, or on carts. Burmese, Chinese, Indians, merchants, shopkeepers, workers, the lifeblood of the city was leaving. We made slow progress on the Sule Pagoda Road. As we crossed the bridge over the railway track and looked over towards the railway station, the area was a mass of would-be evacuees. Some of those on the move were simply heading for the open spaces around the Royal Lakes. We passed the Shwedagon Pagoda as we headed towards the Prome Road, the road jammed with cars, *gharries*, bullock carts and handcarts, all heading in the same direction and out of the city. The Shwedagon rose on its hill, its brilliant golden dome untouched by the morning's catastrophe.

As the Victoria Lakes came into view we could see that there were small groups of people gathering in the dusk all along the shore. Children were bathing at the edge of the lake, little figures just visible in the glow of fires at the waterside. Occasionally, loud cries broke out above the low hum of voices and the broken clatter of cooking pots.

*

I was back in Kokine by the end of the afternoon. Despite the reassurances we'd been giving ourselves, it was a relief to see my father when he arrived back at the Hut earlier than usual. Fran caught him as he came in.

'Bobby tried to get down Strand Road to visit the office after the raid, you know, but he couldn't because there were so many casualties and the ambulances were pushing through.'

He glanced up at me as he was taking a drink from Appaswamy, the family butler. If there was a hint of softness around the eyes, it swiftly disappeared. He threw out, 'Didn't the army have any use for you, Bobby?'

He wasn't looking for a response, so I turned on my heel and went looking for a towel with a notion of having a swim before dinner, despite the freshness of the December evening. Behind the house, the thick jungle foliage was already dark. I took off towards the lake, catching the faint, sweet smell of the frangipani tree. The garden was cool, the bougainvilleas and poinsettias showing up in almost luminous colours in the half light, the two casuarina trees tall, their feathery leaves tracing strange patterns against the dark blue and gold sky. As I reached the lake there was a flash of white as a paddy bird took flight. I was startled for a moment and walked quickly down the steps leading to the water's edge. The dinghy was tied up, together with the other boats, to a row of struts at the side of the water and I clambered into it. Usually there were small lights blinking along the waterside, marking the yacht club. But this evening I could see the far shore only as a shadow beneath the faint purple and pinks of the early evening sky.

I couldn't relax. I'd never been close to my father, but now we had to pull together. Whatever it is that Daddy and Aunt Louisa want from me, I thought, I'll never get it right.

A slight breeze moved across the water, rippling the surface. The *sampans* jostled together, the nearest bumping gently against the dinghy. There would be a few hours until dinner was served, so I unwound the rope and pushed off from the side. It was quite a row across the lake to the club, but it was a good way to get things out of my system. I was still in low spirits when I got to the club jetty, so I sat on the edge, kicking the water with my toe. The club was in blackout and the lights were only a dim yellow haze, but in the fading evening light I could just see the brightly-sashed uniforms and turbans of the bearers as they moved around. There was the occasional clatter of plates and sometimes a voice was carried across the water. But, for the 23 December, there was little sign of the usual party activity.

A figure moved towards me, at first no more than a dark outline, and it took me a little while to see who it was.

'Stapleton, old chap! What are you doing lurking around? We're trying to decide what to do about the club dinner on the 26th. Mustn't let the buggers get to us.'

I'd forgotten about the club dinner. Trust Frank Hurlings to be worried about it as our world collapsed. He worked hard at maintaining a position in the Rangoon social crowd. He was a sandy-haired, pale man in his early thirties with a dispirited-looking moustache, who sucked continuously at his pipe. He had some medical problem which prevented him from joining up. Frank knew Laura's husband, Harry, quite well through his dealings with the Irrawaddy Flotilla Company. He'd come out to Burma shortly before the war and had no family connection with the country that I was aware of.

'How are your folks holding up against all this? Take it they're packing up and going. Must be a dreadful blow.' He sounded genuinely concerned, and I remembered that someone had invited him to one of the tennis parties we'd thrown earlier in the year. I stayed where I was, so he swept the jetty with his hand and sat down, pulling up the immaculate creases of his drill whites slightly.

'I was thinking about what it means to leave all this.' I looked across the water and added, 'Actually, I was thinking about Bassein, where I used to stay as a boy.'

I don't know what made me start spilling my guts to Frank Hurlings, but he looked at me without saying anything, so I carried on. I hadn't thought much about Bassein for years, but now it seemed important. I couldn't read Frank's reaction and carried on, giving him more than I should have done.

'I used to sit on the jetty in Nyeto, just as I am now. It was a small village near Bassein, where we had a country house. If you looked up river past the village, you could see the rice mill chimneys, with their blue-grey smoke twisting upwards.'

As I spoke, I remembered how, as a boy, I used to love walking along the river bank in Bassein, spotting the masts of the boats in the distance. And then there was the gleaming gold of the pagoda, encrusted with diamonds and rubies, rising above the roofs of the town, glorious as it caught the last rays of the sun in the evening.

Frank wasn't looking at me and, without thinking, I added, 'You see, the thing is, you people, those of you who've just come here, you don't love the country the way we do. You just don't know it.'

He stirred uneasily, and then said, 'Ye-es, funny old life. Well, old chap, must get back. Say hello to the folks for me.'

Frank stood for a moment, sucking at his pipe, looking out across the lake, then walked back to the club, his head down, as though he were searching the ground for something. I had embarrassed him – and myself. 'Bobby, you're a fool,' I said out loud.

There was a chill to the December night, but I stripped off my clothes, threw them into the bottom of the boat and swam energetically out towards one of the small islands, and then turned over onto my back. While I'd been talking to Frank, darkness had fallen in the sudden way that it did in Burma, like a curtain dropping. The sky was now a deep blue-black, but the moon was bright and a few stars were already out, so that the edge of the lake and the outline of the islands emerged as ghostly shapes. Everything was peaceful and reassuring; it was barely credible that the same sky had harboured the Japanese bombers so few hours before. I heard a gentle movement to my side and saw a ripple, and could just make out the small head of a water snake gliding past. I remembered that, before he married Laura,

Harry used to swim across the lake with his pals in the evening from his chummery – the house he shared with other young company men. His laughter, which he threw out as two low barks, would echo across the tennis courts in the evening as they made their way back up to the Hut. Mad, bad Harry, my sisters used to call him, Marcie laughing behind her hand and rolling her eyes. The man had a bit of a reputation with the girls. Good times! I turned over and swam slowly back to the shore.

*

It was nearly eight-thirty when I arrived back. Harry was already there, a tall man in his mid-forties, with handsome, regular features. He modelled himself on Tyrone Power, a popular screen idol of the day; he had thick, black hair which he slicked back, and wore a small moustache. When I walked across the lawn towards the bungalow, he was sitting together with my father on the veranda of the Hut, smoking a cigar. Aunt Louisa was looking impatient, her back rigid in the large rattan chair, with her face somewhat turned away, twisting one of her rings with its large jade stone round and round on her forefinger. I didn't like Harry; he was too cocky and not my type, but Laura was married to him and I tried to get on with the chap. That evening, I didn't feel like talking to him.

'Hey, Bobby,' he called out to me, as Appaswamy ran to meet me with a fresh towel. 'What the hell are you doing going out swimming tonight of all nights? The Japs could come over while you are out communing with the stars.'

He waved a glass in my direction, and I muttered back that I was going to change. I felt irritated by the man, but tried to put him out of my mind. Once Laura had left he would be on his own and we would all have to stick with each other.

I felt better when I joined them later. Aunt Louisa had gone in, and I could hear her calling out to Fran from inside the Hut. I went in briefly to see them. Laura was worried about whether Aunt Louisa and Fran would be able to leave as planned in January.

'People are saying that all the Indian coolies are streaming out of Rangoon, and it seems as though the docks may just come to a standstill if they go.'

I responded blandly with the words that were going round HQ that afternoon, 'It's a panic reaction, Laura. You will see, some of them won't go very far. If there's no raid tonight, they'll probably turn back. The government's going to do everything it can to keep people in Rangoon.'

But it was worrying. The Posts and Telegraph people were staying put and waiting on orders, but it was the casual Indian labour that kept much of Rangoon ticking over, and they were now on the road with their few possessions on their heads.

'Look at the hospitals! How can they cope with all the wounded? They are saying that even in the hospitals not only the coolies but the nurses and some of the officials are going too.' Laura was insistent. 'How was the Prome Road when you came, Bobby? Harry said that you can't move along there tonight and people don't even know where they are going. If there's another raid just now, it'll be complete panic.'

'They're just scared, the poor things,' said Fran. Her warm, dark vowels were nervous and exaggerated. The words jostled together. 'It's much safer for us out here. And for all the government's fine words, it's their own people who've started this panic. Harry was saying that the officials are seizing any boat they can and paying huge sums of money, and sending their own wives away on them.' Her voice had risen, the tone sharp. Then she stopped and continued more gently, 'Well, we are all deciding we have to leave. How can you blame them? I don't blame them, do you Laura?' She pursed her lips, and her voice ended upwards, questioning, but it was not a question that needed an answer.

We were all silent. Then Fran turned to me again, steadying herself against a chair with her hand, 'Robert is arranging for a Mrs Burrage to take over a lease on the Hut and transfer her boarding house here where it's a bit safer.'

I moved out to the veranda and sat down, watching my father talking to Harry. My father looked smart in his fawn, lightweight suit. He had a long face, burnt from the sun and accentuated by a somewhat full, dark beard, which contrasted with the near whiteness of his hair. His deep, sloping forehead was lined, and his eyes, like Louisa's, were a surprising blue. He didn't look at me now or acknowledge my presence in any way. Appaswamy was hovering by the drinks table, and I signalled to him to pour me a peg.

Harry was waving his glass about and his voice was too loud.

'Some of our own Burmese servants are probably fifth columnists,' he was saying, 'and if they realise that they're going to have to face the Japs, you don't think for one minute they are going to stay with us? No!'

Appaswamy moved silently back into the living room.

'I don't think you're right, Harry.' My father put his glass down on the table, his face darkening as he was caught by a fit of coughing. 'It's only some of the *thajee* in the villages, who've been persuaded by the Free Burma Army zealots. Bound to happen, but most of the Burmans are far too loyal to join the enemy.'

I could see that my father was tense, but Harry never seemed to be thrown by him. There was a certain brittle confidence about Harry.

'Loyal to whom? Do you think they really care what happens to the British now? Why should they care, Robert? If it's one of ours, or a Chinese, or a Jap, it's all the same. Why not? You don't really think they love the great British Empire?'

My father just stared at him, then said, 'You see, if you'd spent time in the villages the way I have, Harry, you would understand more.'

Harry sank back into his chair and waved his foot in the silence. I slapped my own ankle where the mosquitoes were biting above the line of my sock, relieved to hear the bell for dinner. As we went into the dining room, I caught my father.

'Daddy, what's this agreement with Mrs Burrage?'

'Once Louisa and Fran have left, the idea is that she will come in and bring some of her boarders with her. We men are going to be coming and going, and at least it means the place will be looked after, and we'll have a roof over our heads when we need it.' He smiled faintly. 'It's not easy, is it, my boy? But with any luck we'll be back here in a few months. The girls – all of us. We'll have a good Christmas next year.'

Dinner was a sad affair. There were probably thousands dead in the city, but we followed the rituals of our daily life in Rangoon as if in doing so we could hold on to it all. None of us read in each other's eyes, or in those of the servants, as they served drinks, drove our cars, dug our gardens as they always did, the message that was surely going around in the villages and the bazaars: *It's nearly over.*

3

BOBBY

January 1942

During the next few weeks, I was in and out of Rangoon, checking on the communication lines and reporting back to HQ. Rangoon had been hit by some eighty Japanese bombers on 23 December, killing two thousand or more people. Then, on Christmas Day, the Japanese hit the city a second time, doing even more damage. There were close on one hundred bombers and a number of fighters, but our boys in their Buffaloes and the American Tomahawks gave them a rough time. In the days following, driving along the Prome Road between Kokine and the city, or out towards Mingaladon Airport, I passed the Japanese fighter wrecks lying in the fields. We badly needed some consolation because, after the Christmas Day bombings, the Japanese came over regularly at night. Even from Kokine, we could hear the dreaded wail of the sirens and the terrible thud of the bombs dropping.

The rush from Rangoon, which started after the first raid, became even worse after Christmas Day. Travelling north out of town became a nightmare. Most of the crowds of evacuees spilling onto the Prome Road by foot or in any vehicle they could lay their hands on, had their eyes set on routes to India. In fact, during that period just after Christmas, there was a total confusion of terrified people coming and going. With the city threatening to come to a standstill, the authorities reacted quickly and got out to the refugee camps, trying to persuade the evacuees to come back to get things running again. They convinced quite a lot of them that Rangoon wouldn't ever fall into enemy hands so, by the beginning of January, the trains coming back to Rangoon were full of Indian coolie labour returning, even though at the same time the officials' families were still streaming up to Upper Burma in cars, lorries and river launches.

*

I spent much of January along the Pegu route. Pegu was about fifty miles north-east of Rangoon, and hanging on to it was crucial if we were to stop the Japanese advance on the city. I was happy in my own way to be out on the road with Ismail. I had my jeep and my priority rating for petrol; I was supplied with a sten gun and carried my Smith and Wesson in my belt. My job was as far as possible to liaise with Post and Telecommunications to see that personnel were being evacuated when necessary, maintaining forward communications and at the same time keeping the army in touch with the situation. It was the civilians, in fact, who kept the telegraph lines in operation and my job was to go round to the postal centres, checking that the army could use the lines at any time they needed to. What they would do was to tap into them, send a local chap up to clip onto the line and start signalling that way.

In early January, Japanese troops were making swift and alarming progress through Lower Burma. Tavoy was a small tin mining centre and port; it was a disaster when it was captured on 19 January because it marked the start of the British retreat. Shortly afterwards, British troops withdrew from Mergui. The Japanese then attacked Moulmein on the mouth of the Salween River on 30 January, nearly two hundred miles east of Rangoon, and the following day our men withdrew across the river. That was the signal for the Japanese to advance into Central and Upper Burma.

Robert – my father – was too old to fight, but clung for a long time to the idea that he could do something to help the war effort in Burma. Meanwhile, he kept on with his insurance work. There were a lot of outbreaks of fires in Central Burma in the warehouses and factories, so he was kept busy; often the fires were started for the insurance money and it was his job to assess the causes and make a full report. And once the raids started, he was appointed as a government assessor for the fires started by the bombing.

Ba Yee attached himself to my father and travelled around with him on his fire insurance work. There were times when the men were all on the road, leaving the women with the head *mali* and the *chowkidar* guarding the house. Lion was still in Pegu, waiting for a posting out, becoming increasingly exasperated with the authorities. Mrs Burrage decided not to move in and left for Upper Burma, and the house began to have an empty, neglected feel, with books and bed linen stacked and ready to be taken out and stored.

I had a few days to spend in Rangoon towards the end of January. Laura had an itinerary organised for her land route across the border into India at Tamu, through to Imphal and to the rail head at Dimapur. From there she was going to take the train and join the Family in Calcutta. The cook and his wife, who had been nanny to the girls, had left Rangoon early in January, and some of the servants followed their lead.

When I arrived I found Aunt Louisa and Fran busy packing up the house and making detailed lists of the household effects to be sent to the *godowns*.

I went from room to room, peering into boxes to see what was being packed up. The living room was already beginning to look bare. The large oil painting and several of the water colours had been taken off the walls. The silk curtains swept down and across the bare walls onto the heavily-polished floor, left there to provide blackout cover. The Chinese rugs were in rolls against the walls, but the large living-room carpet, with its deep blues and greens, was to be stored later, together with most of the teak furniture, my father's carved writing desk and an elaborate, fan-backed chair. The docks were in chaos, and getting our things to the *godowns* was proving difficult; it looked unlikely that we would get half of it shipped.

Looking into the dining room, I could see that the heavy sideboards were stripped of much of their silver and the little table, which usually contained a large silver tray and teapot, had been removed. Most of the books had been emptied from the bookshelves, and Ba Yee's young cousin was packing them into wooden crates.

I found Fran and Aunt Louisa wrapping up and packing pieces of porcelain and glass in my aunt's bedroom, a task it seemed they didn't want to trust to the servants.

My aunt smiled up at me from beside one of the packing cases. 'Come on in, Bobby. We're finishing up in a minute anyway. I'm exhausted from all this bending. Harry brought in these crates for us, so we're getting on with it, packing it up until it's all over.'

Fran looked up at me and spoke quickly. 'You know, Bobby, we are going to have to leave the refrigerator here. What can we do? Even if we were to leave it with someone else, they will probably be going soon.'

Poor Fran! The electricity had been wired into the Hut not long before and the intensely desired refrigerator, object of great pride and delight, all sparkling white and gleaming chrome, had arrived just before Christmas. She gave me a painful smile that didn't reach her eyes, a look that was familiar when she was unhappy or worried. I gave her a kiss and made my excuses, going off to see if I could be useful in the rest of the house.

*

I went over to my aunt Bea's on the second day I was in Rangoon. She and her husband, Lester, lived in the Mansion on the Prome Road, just before the road swept around and cleft the lakes in two – a huge, porticoed white house, built less than ten years earlier. I kept the engine running while the *mali* opened up the ornate front gates. Crows were wheeling above my head, cawing hideously and sweeping down onto a heap of rubbish on the road outside. Whatever the officials were saying, services were packing up. Driving through the avenue of palm trees which lined the driveway, I noticed that the garden was beginning to show signs of neglect.

In the house I looked over the polished banister as I went up the central staircase and could see the door to the dining room ajar, the sunlight gleaming on the teak panelling. No one was around. I carried on up to the sitting room which gave onto the veranda and called out. My cousin Issie was in her room packing things up and came out to join me. Her face was puffy and she was beginning to look heavily pregnant; she was wearing a thin sort of dress and shuffled into the room in embroidered slippers. Her hair was pinned into tight waves and I could see where the dark hair was beginning to show through the dyed blonde.

'Mums is lying down.' Issie spoke under her breath. 'We are going up in the Chev to Maymyo tomorrow. She doesn't want to move at all but I don't know how I can possibly have the baby here in these conditions. We are all scared to death every time the bombers come over and we don't even know if I will be able to find someone to help when baby is born.'

'Where is Aunt Babs?'

'Goodness knows.' I wasn't sure if Issie sounded scornful or envious; her precise tones always had a supercilious edge. 'She's probably decided that as this is the last she'll see of any decent social life for a while, it's best to make the most of it. They held quite a big dinner dance at the Minto Gardens last night – a sort of farewell thing – and Auntie Babs went with some of her crowd who are still here.'

My aunts Bea and Babs were my mother's two sisters, and quite different from each other. Babs was the youngest of the three, and everyone said she took after my grandfather, an Italian. A man of spirit, Laura said, but Aunt Louisa's mouth always set firm when he was mentioned. As a child I was aware that Babs's name came up in whispered conversations that were hastily terminated, that sentences were left unfinished. Bea was different.

'Aunt Bea?' I knocked gently on her door and looked into the room. The shutters were half closed across the windows, so that shafts of light still streamed in. The blades of the ceiling fan turned noisily to their own rhythm, the heavy air moving swathes of mosquito netting across the bed.

'Bo-bby? I thought I heard your voice. I will join you. You will eat something with us?' The soft, high vowels that came from the bed were slightly muffled.

I went onto the veranda that ran the length of the house and soon heard Aunt Bea calling down over the stairs to the Madrassi cook.

'Raman! *Sappadu kontuvaa!* Bring some snacks and water also.'

Juno, my uncle Lester's old golden labrador, was lying in the afternoon heat, her head between her paws. She twitched, opened one eye, and her tail stirred slightly in recognition as I sat down in the cane chair. Issie had followed me out to the doorway and stood framed, clipping her hair at the back of her neck, dark sweat marks under her arms.

'We hear you've had letters from Marcie. They seem to have found their feet in Calcutta.' She looked across the compound and screwed up her eyes a little. 'The way I feel right now, I shall be glad to go. Trust me to have a baby arriving at this precise moment. Whatever they say, I feel as though we're just waiting around for the Japanese to get here, and you hear such terrible stories – things that have been happening in Tavoy and round there . . . Or else we shall all be bombed in our beds. I can't stand listening to those things coming over every night.' She tossed her head up towards the clear, pale sky.

Issie's younger sister and brother had left for India earlier in January while she was persuaded to stay on to have the baby. No doubt my cousin felt nervous in her condition and with her husband away, but she irritated me. I felt claustrophobic coming back to Rangoon, and it would be good to hit the road again. I changed the subject.

'Are you taking Juno with you to Maymyo?'

'Of course we are! We couldn't leave you behind, could we, you dear old thing. Mind you, she's off her food. Maybe she would rather rest her poor old bones here in Rangoon.'

Juno lifted a brow and twitched, waving her paw at a bothersome fly.

*

I was hot and leaned over the edge of the veranda. The grass hadn't been watered for some time and the lawn was spoiled, with yellowish-brown patches in places. The mango tree threw a shadow across the grass and the veranda was shaded by hanging ferns. A thin Burman in a deep blue *longyi* and checked *gaung baung* on his head walked slowly up the front drive, carrying a shallow tin basin of dried fish, his thonged sandals scuffing the hot dust in front of him. He went to the back of the house, the acrid smell of fish lingering as he passed.

Aunt Bea called me in from the veranda. She was never strong, but she was looking thinner than ever, her face drawn.

'We are in quite a state, Bobby. The cook has disappeared. For three days we have had no sweeper and so we have to do all the sanitations ourselves. Now I am just worrying, you see. We are driving to Maymyo tomorrow, but we have nowhere to put our things. Look at all my music, Bobby, and my lovely piano. Once the house is left, *dacoits* will come and destroy everything . . .' She tailed off and wiped her brow and neck with a handkerchief.

Aunt Bea was one of the musicians in the family. My father played the piano and was a good cellist. Both my sisters took after him. Laura played the violin like an angel, but for my aunt Bea the piano was her passion. She was a nervous type, the enervating air of Rangoon exhausting her, and she had little real taste for bridge sessions and the other activities that absorbed Rangoon society. But at evening parties we would beg her to open the piano and she would willingly abandon any conversation to play Beethoven sonatas or Chopin nocturnes, her slender fingers tripping over the keys, her polished finger nails making a gentle tapping noise. She would just as happily break into some ragtime music or strum out *Roll out the Barrel*, or *Hang out the Washing on the Seigfried Line*, or we would pass her sheet music from the latest show. I glanced over to where piles of music still filled the bottom shelves of the glass-fronted cupboard.

'Why don't I stay here when I can, Auntie? And there is no reason why I can't bring up the music and anything else you want when I get up to Maymyo. Please stop worrying!'

Moving into my aunt's house would be an easy enough task. I carried a change of clothing and my bedroll with me, and I was used to putting it down wherever there was sleeping space. Ismail had his own quarters while we were at HQ. The only problem was how long I was going to be able to stay in Rangoon.

*

I had another call to make, so I decided to leave if I was going to return and install myself at Bea's that night. As I left, I heard Issie's shrill voice raised and against it my aunt's soft, tired tones.

I was heading for the Lamonts' bungalow. It was in Rangoon itself, on one of the roads which cross-cut each other at right angles. The streets of the city were filthy and smelling foul, with piles of rubbish left uncollected and rotting in the heat. One of the cinemas was still open, but the bazaars and shops were shuttered up, and shattered glass from the shop windows was lying in the deserted streets. It was a depressing sight. I turned left off the main road and drove onto one of the gravel driveways. The Lamonts lived in a small timber and brick bungalow, what we called *semi-pucca*, set back off the road and almost obscured by the dark-leaved mango trees in the garden. I felt the slight excitement I always felt when seeing Eva Lamont, but it was her father who came out to greet me.

'Bobby!' He put his arm affectionately round my shoulders. 'It's good to see you! What are you doing in Rangoon? We're all trying to get away, you know, and I thought you were out on the road somewhere. Tell me, did your aunt get the boat all right?'

'Not yet,' I said, 'but they're going in a couple of days.'

Paul Lamont was a gaunt man in his early sixties. He was always rather shabbily dressed, his ill-fitting tropical suit frayed at the edges. He wore his shirt without a tie, open at the neck. Lamont had retired after working for years with one of the timber companies, and the family were comfortable enough on his small pension. It seemed to me that he had developed a somewhat cynical attitude towards Rangoon's social scene during his years of living in camp, with no time for the demands of etiquette and the petty regulations of Rangoon polite society.

That suited me fine. I never saw him without a *beedi* of some strong local tobacco at his lips, which he would throw away half smoked. His wife was a thin, nervous Burmese woman who always looked uncomfortable with life. She came towards me now, her eyes red-rimmed.

'How are you, Auntie?' I took both her hands.

'She's being stubborn.' Lamont spoke for her. 'She says she won't move out of the house.'

'Take some food with us, Bobby. How is your father?' Daw Min Min ignored her husband.

'You can't fight the Japanese on your own, Auntie,' I tried to joke. 'It's a terrible thing, but everyone's going,' I added in Burmese.

'This is my house and I'm not going to leave it now,' she replied, suddenly vehement. Then she added, 'Did you hear that the Japanese have been dropping leaflets in east Rangoon? They say they won't harm local people.'

'That's not the point,' I said, more harshly than I intended. 'How are you going to live here? Where are you going to get food? Soon there won't even be any water to be had at all.' Daw Min Min's mouth set in a thin line, and I turned to Lamont. 'What are you planning to do?' He was hovering by the door, still looking at his wife, and I added, 'By the way, where is Eva?'

'She's out on a quest for open shops,' Lamont said, turning to me with a weak smile. 'My daughter can't live without the shops, so we're going to have to leave! Seriously, Eva is scared out of her wits now, although she doesn't say so. Most of her friends have already gone.'

*

Eva arrived back in the early evening and was surprised to see me.

'Hello, look who's dropped in from the skies! Where have you appeared from? We haven't seen you for so long we thought you'd forgotten about poor us!' Eva had a way of talking which made it difficult to make any reply. I laughed.

'You know they don't let me stay anywhere for very long these days. Sometimes I'm only in Rangoon for a couple of hours.' I added, 'You look nice.'

'You're too kind!' She made a mock bow and sank onto one of the chairs. She was wearing a *longyi* in bright blues and pinks and a short, Burmese-style blouse; her thick, dark waves had been pulled back off her face and were studded with flowers. Issie had mentioned that some of the Anglo-Burmese girls were abandoning European dress in the hope that they would be less visible to fifth columnists. Issie had been scornful, but it suited Eva. She had a beautiful oval face, with high, rounded cheekbones, and to my mind an infinitely expressive mouth.

I had fallen in love with Eva in 1940 during a holiday in Kalaw, a hill station south of Mandalay. At the time, Paul Lamont had just retired, and he and his wife had rented a bungalow there for the season, inviting young people to stay as paying guests – an idea that was all the rage at the time. I was quite a loner and spent much of my time on my motor bike, but that year a pal of mine persuaded me to stay in one of those bungalows, and we went up on our bikes. And that's how I met Eva.

There was quite a crowd of us; we slept on the floor, all of us mucking in together, and we had good fun. Kalaw had a marvellous climate and was surrounded by thickly-wooded hills. The bungalows there were beautiful, set back from winding roads. We used to wander down to the open-air market and buy fruit – mangoes, guavas and pomelos – from the hill women, with their colourful dress and huge silver collars and ear pendants. We would go for walks in the countryside around and, in the evenings, Eva tried to teach me to dance to the old gramophone. Of course, she didn't take me seriously; she must have known that I had seriously fallen for her and that suited her very well. On my last evening we walked over to the golf links. Eva stopped and took hold of my arm and said, 'Don't you just love the smell of those gorgeous pines?' It reminded me of a scene from the films, so I kissed her. She laughed at me and simply said, 'Promise you won't do that again!' But she held my hand all the way back to the club and we arranged to meet again when she returned to Rangoon.

Eva practised hard at her innocent-girl image, and I was quite happy to play along with it so long as she carried on seeing me. She was just twenty years old then and had started working as a government stenographer. In fact, I soon realised that her sights were set much higher than me. We never did go out together in any real sense and I settled in to a role of older brother. I didn't stop loving her, but in some ways our relationship made me somewhat harder. Perhaps I came to understand and accept what she wanted from me, and I grew up a little.

*

'It's almost impossible to get a taxi.' Eva was addressing the room now. 'Most of the taxiwallahs have left, and the ones that are still here are rude and charging such outrageous fares. Oh, guess who I saw in Phayre Street, although I can't imagine what she's still doing in Rangoon. I would have thought she would have been safely in the hills by now.' She looked at me pointedly.

'Who?'

'Your girlfriend, Doris Godfrey.'

I shook my head at Eva. I was about twenty-two years old when I encountered Doris Godfrey – it was before I met Eva. I was working at Philips at the time as a radio engineer and was doing quite well. I used to go out in the evenings to customers' houses after they had a radio fitted to see how they were getting on, and that's how I met Doris. She was a lovely girl, and very elegant. Her mother was from one of the hill tribes and her teeth were badly stained from the cheroots she was constantly smoking. She had married a government servant; she was very ambitious for her daughter and had her educated in India – in one of the convents in Mussoorie. Doris was somewhat of an 'it girl' of her day; she didn't have a job as far as I was aware and she moved in a different social crowd from me. I used to see her at the cinema with some of the rich young men in Rangoon and I couldn't get her off my mind.

I probably told Lion about my obsession with this girl, as he never stopped teasing me for not asking her out. He must have persuaded me, for one day I bumped into her in Whiteaway's department store and asked her to come to the cinema with me. I borrowed Lion's car; it was a beautiful Chev and I arrived with flowers, and did everything I could to turn the date into a special occasion. But she wasn't impressed and I never did understand why she'd agreed to come out with me in the first place. When we got to the cinema she sat bolt upright and I didn't dare even put my arm round her. In fact, the atmosphere was so strained that my heart sank with every minute. At the end of the film, I took her downstairs to the soda fountain and ordered her an ice cream and milk shake. Then afterwards there was nothing to do but to take her straight home.

It took me a long time to recover from that experience, because I was obsessed with the girl. What upset me most was that for me it was all a big thing, a special occasion, whereas she took it all for granted and hardly seemed to notice me the whole evening. I didn't dare go back to her house, but about a month later I saw her out in a *gharry* with a girlfriend and I must have decided I wanted to say something, because I called out 'Doris!' and steered my motor bike alongside them, thinking they would stop. I thought they hadn't seen me, but then Doris said something in her companion's ear and they both turned round to me, lifting up the edge of their wide-brimmed hats. Doris had a faint smile on her lips. Then she tugged at her friend and they turned back, their heads close together. I stopped the bike at the side of the road and watched the *gharry* moving ahead through the traffic.

I heard later that Doris had married an army major. He was twice her age, and there were rumours about his life style – he was the sort of chap who spent his evenings in the gaming clubs and bars of the Chinese quarter down by the docks, but kept it quiet from the ladies. A year later, in one of the long, comfortable evenings in Kalaw, I found myself confiding in Eva about her predecessor in my affections. Then, back in Rangoon, I found out where Doris lived and went to visit her early one evening. She was alone in the house with her servants and there was an air of brooding excitement about her, a faint smell of alcohol on her breath. Her cheeks were highly rouged and she looked very thin, her flowered dress held in tightly by a belt. I remember being struck by her shoes, which were white and had very high heels and enormous bows on the front. She seemed pleased to see me and greeted me like an old friend, and wanted to know any news I had of her crowd. I felt sorry that I'd come and after fifteen minutes or so started making excuses. As I stepped onto the veranda, stretching out my hand, Doris took it and said suddenly, 'Darling, you were rather sweet!' and kissed me urgently on the mouth.

In the months that followed, I often wondered if Doris had been issuing me an invitation, and there were occasions when I thought I might go back and find out. But my old feelings for her had gone and, anyway, if there were an invitation, I had no wish to be involved. The whole set-up looked rather seedy to me, and I decided to steer well clear of it.

Looking at Eva now, laughing at me, I resisted any temptation to ask how Doris had looked, but simply said, 'You're a dreadful tease, child. I haven't thought about Doris for years.'

I turned to Daw Min Min. 'You see what Eva was saying about the taxiwallahs, Auntie. Everyone is getting out of Rangoon. In a week or two, if you stay, you'll be the only one left.'

But it was obvious that nothing would move her and I made my way back to Kokine feeling anxious to be on the road again.

*

Aunt Louisa and Fran left for India by boat shortly after my visit and they were lucky to get a passage when they did. Laura went by road to Mandalay some two weeks later to join a group trekking out across the Naga Hills. Harry was regarded as essential personnel, but he had business up-country with the company, so was able to travel with her as far as Mawlaik.

By 10 February, Martaban was in enemy hands and the Japanese crossed the Salween at Pa-an. A week later saw the fiercest fighting of the campaign at the Bilin River crossing when our troops were held for two days of close-quarters jungle fighting. They retreated back about thirty miles or so to the Sittang Bridge, but we lost a lot of men.

That was a point in the Japanese advance which stuck in my mind because I was staying with my cousin Lion in Pegu on the night of the 16th. It was important to hold Pegu, with its key position on the Rangoon-Mandalay railway and its closeness to Rangoon itself. But things were looking bleak. Lion had been posted to the district court but was spending his days travelling back and forth to Rangoon, trying to get permission to get out of Pegu before the army commandeered all the jeeps and he became stranded.

That evening there was a constant stream of visitors to the old government-owned house, and the only topic of conversation was whether the Japanese advance could be halted. The house was situated on a knoll overlooking the trunk road. Convoys of lorries, trucks and station wagons carrying war goods mustered in long lines just outside the court compound and within a stone's throw of the balcony; they were passing on their way through to Mandalay, Maymyo and Lashio to cross the China border.

Singapore had fallen the day before, a disaster that had sent shock waves through us all. There had been an air raid on Pegu that afternoon; Lion was low and dispirited, convinced that Burma was next in line to fall. There was little doubt that our people hadn't counted on either the Japanese fighting skill or the apathy of the Burmans, faced with the possible collapse of the British raj. There was a cry of Burma for the Burmans around at the time; in the thirties, the *Dobama Asi-ayone*, the Free Burma Association, had become popular in some circles. At the university there were some young nationalists who called themselves *thakins*; they looked to the example of Gandhi and the nationalist movement in India, and you could always spot them in their homespun cotton *longyis* and sandals. Then, with the new constitution and administration in place from 1937, there were elected Burmese government ministers and the British took more of a back seat.

My feeling was that too much was being made of any threat to the war effort. The Burmese troops were a lot more loyal than people gave them credit for. But Lion was in one of his contrary, cynical moods and we came close to quarrelling.

'Don't be so naïve, boy,' he roared at me, 'or are you one of those who can't accept that the British can be unpopular anywhere?'

'That's not what I said, brother,' I muttered.

He pulled nervously at his beard and jabbed his finger at me, taking no notice.

'Look at the way we've treated the Burmans in the commercial world. You know perfectly well we pay them at a completely different rate from the Anglo-Indians and in Indian companies they're not employed at all. And what's our excuse? That the Burmans aren't suited to commerce! But we don't give them a chance, do we? And now we're surprised at the result.'

I didn't care to argue with Lion, and I hoped the discussion would drop. I looked at him; he was a short, energetic figure, somewhat bizarre-looking in his black, creased trousers and jacket.

'Murthi!'

Lion drank endless quantities of soda water, which Murthi would lace with lime and crushed ice. He brought it in now, silent in bare feet, balancing the tray on the fingers of one hand. Lion had officially been on the wagon for some months, having forsworn all alcohol with a great flourish, but I couldn't help wondering how long it would last, given his increasing frustrations with the bureaucracy. He wasn't going to let the topic rest just yet.

'You know what they think of European businessmen? I'll tell you: that they are an unscrupulous bunch out to scupper Burmese interests at the first opportunity. And the lot at the university are regarded as a load of cranks and the leavings of English universities. Probably right! The only Europeans that the Burmans have any respect for at all are the missionaries, and I'm not sure about them. Why should the ordinary Burman regard this as his war?'

He drew on a short pipe, holding the bowl carefully in his cupped hand and then continued in the slightly melodramatic tone that he sometimes adopted.

'You know there is a very old mystic saying that the Burmans have.' He stared at me, and then continued, '*The hintha bird will be destroyed by the hunter, the hunter will be hit by the umbrella rod and the umbrella rod will be struck by the thunderbolt.*'

'And what's that all about?' I asked.

'I'm about to tell you! The hintha bird is supposed to be the Mons, the people who conquered Ava, the Irrawaddy Delta. The hunter is Alaungpaya, who defeated the Mons and founded the Burmese dynasty. And the umbrella rod, my dear boy, is the British who deposed the last king of the Alaungpaya dynasty. No one knew who the thunderbolt was, that would dislodge the British, but now the head of the Burma Independence Army has taken on the name of Bo Mogyo, or Thunderbolt.' Lion looked at me, raised his eyebrows and lifted his lime and soda: 'Chin chin!'

Although Lion and I were cousins, he was more than twenty years older than me. His sisters adored him, humoured his eccentricities and tolerated his faults. That was the thing about the Family: they always stood by their own. And for me, I did look up to the man. He had the rank of colonel as well as his legal qualifications, and he was a seasoned Chinese scholar. When I was young, he was in many ways my mentor and bought me my first motor bike when I was fourteen. He was an affectionate person in his own way, and my father wasn't around in those days. Once I'd moved out of the Hut and into the bungalow next door with Lion, we became quite close. He was a bit of a lad, gambled heavily and was a great one for the women. He had one or two lady friends at the yacht club and was seen around town with some of the unmarried literary types in Rangoon – and it wasn't unknown for him to pay attention to married ones as well. When he stayed out all night the Family frowned inwardly, but no one would say anything to him.

Once, when I'd just started at the university, Lion took me for a meal in the Chinese quarter. In fact, it was more of a night club than a restaurant, holding a nightly cabaret with a bar at one side of the room, the atmosphere smoke-filled; I'd never been to a place like that before. They had a girl there who danced for the customers and I was terrified that she would come over to our table. She wore a skirt in some flimsy material, cut low at the hips, and she had a sort of brief top on. She moved round between the tables, thrusting her hips in an absurdly erotic dance. I found it all very embarrassing.

Lion gave me a nudge. 'Ignore her, old chap, if you have to, but she's quite harmless, you know, so don't be so nervous.'

He had a way of twinkling his brown eyes, of looking at you, so you could see what the women were drawn to. There was something irresponsible about Lion for a man of his position. We were always borrowing money from each other and, when there was none to borrow, he would go to my aunt Louisa and she would never refuse him. He had a youthfulness, a quality which made him extraordinarily attractive, but which could also be quite infuriating.

*

The following evening I was still in Pegu and passed a group of men squatting around a brazier near the bazaar, making tea. A tall, dark-skinned man was sitting on his haunches with his arms covering his face. As I drove past, he turned his head and looked across at us. I was certain I'd seen him somewhere before, stopped the jeep and sent Ismail over to him. I watched Ismail gesture towards me, and the man stood up painfully and walked across to us. He was carrying a thick layer of dust about him, although I could make out that his clothes were in good-enough condition. And then I remembered him.

'Aren't you one of the servants in Dick Smith's household?' I asked him.

The Smiths came from the Tavoy area, but I had met Dick at university and had once ridden down on the bike to visit his family. Dick later married a pretty girl – a childhood sweetheart – and I lost touch with them, although I heard that he was now serving as a district officer in Tavoy.

The man shook his head from side to side in assent.

'Yes, sahib. Kureeya, sahib.'

'Where is Dick Baba, Kureeya?'

Kureeya didn't answer me but looked away slowly, turning his head to one side, and then passed two hands across his face, first the left, then the right.

'Dick Baba is taken, sahib, in Tavoy itself.'

'What do you mean? Captured?'

'Yes, sahib.'

'Where is the memsahib?'

'She went to Mandalay, sahib. I have been staying here only, but now . . .' Kureeya looked at the ground. His whole body seemed to curve in a gesture of despair.

'You must go and find her,' I said. 'Listen,' I added, 'jump in the jeep. I'll take you to the station and you must get a train from there.'

When we arrived, the town was already in the throes of evacuating and the scenes at the station were appalling. We abandoned the jeep a hundred yards from the station forecourt and had to force our way through the crowds. The noise that surged towards us in the booking area was an assault of shouts in a dozen languages. Images seemed to detach themselves from the scene. A large-bellied man, dabbing constantly at the beads of sweat around his neck and face, was haranguing a station official while his wife waited, with bulging leather cases. The eldest child clutched a large, awkward bundle tied up in a white cloth and the two youngest held on to her skirts. A porter pushed past, his back and legs bent, his arms curved upwards to steady the pile of baggage carried on his head. Beyond, there were bells clanging above the clamour as people struggled to board trains that were full beyond all possible limits, hanging on the side rails and clambering onto the tops of the carriages. I gave Kureeya twelve rupees and last saw him disappearing into the throng of people, his tall figure unusual for a south Indian, with his carelessly tied head cloth marking his movement through the crush. The babble of voices in the station was deafening and above it I could hear the cries of the *chaiwallahs* as they carried their trays of hot sweet tea high above the crowd. Near me a child was screaming incessantly. I pushed my way back out of the station, headed for the jeep, found Ismail, and took the road to Rangoon.

4

CHRISSIE

January 1986

I drove out to Hertfordshire a few weeks after Christmas. It was an early January day that held little promise for the spring to come; there was a faint fog in the air, the countryside on either side of the A10 bleak and colourless. When I arrived, the cottage, by contrast, was warm and inviting. My father greeted me cheerfully, and we engaged in our almost ritual exchange.

'How's school?' he said. 'Term started, I suppose.'

'Yup, afraid so.'

'How are the kids?'

'The usual,' I said, hanging up my coat. 'Pretty awful.'

After lunch we settled down with cups of coffee. I wanted to know more about the Family in the Burma days, before the war engulfed their lives so suddenly. Since I had first brought him my grandfather's letters, my father seemed increasingly at ease with his memories and had started to talk more freely.

Now he said, 'I suppose this is important to you, Chrissie.'

I just nodded. He placed his cup down in its saucer.

'We were well off, you see, very comfortable. As you know, in those days, during the wartime, the Family were all living in Kokine, which was just outside Rangoon, and in the hot weather we all went off to the hills. Everyone did if they could; you couldn't stand the heat.'

'What about the house in Bassein that your father had?' I had gone to the library and found Bassein on a map, a town about 120 miles west of Rangoon, lying on the river, in the Irrawaddy delta.

'Well, when I was a boy, Daddy owned a timber and paddy business in Bassein and I used to go there during my school holidays.' My father's voice grew stronger. 'We also had a country bungalow, built quite high on stilts, in a little fishing hamlet about twelve miles from there. If you can imagine, Chrissie, you could see all the nets laid out drying in the sun; and you could walk along the open road to where the rich traders and merchants lived, with gardens that swept right down to the road.'

He was moving his hands about, remembering, enthusiastic.

'The river was about a mile or so wide opposite our house and on the other bank there were vast fields of rice and prairies of tiger grass. Most of the shipping was upstream, opposite the town, and you could see columns of smoke coming up from the funnels of the steamers . . . But, you see, whether we still had the Nyeto house at that time, during the war . . . I don't think so.'

He got up to pour me a sherry, the cork easing out of the bottle with a gentle, familiar sigh, then brought over two glasses, spilling it a little.

'Tell me, Dad,' I said, changing the subject, 'how on earth did Lion and Mouse get their names? I've never really thought about it before.'

My father looked up at me with his wide, open smile that always showed his teeth a little, as if he were about to laugh.

'Huh! Well, as you know, Lion's name was actually Lionel. He was the eldest and the story was that Mouse, who was the next one, always called him Lion when she was little and I think he called her Mouse in return because she was such a thin little scrap. You know the story . . .'

'Oh yes, of course, *The Lion and the Mouse.*'

'Anyway, her real name was Annabel, but the only person who ever used it was my aunt Louisa when she was angry. And believe me, she could get angry.'

He blew his lips out, his eyes wide, shaking his head slightly.

'Of course, my cousins were closer to my father's generation, and they were the ones we all turned to in the household. Laura was another cousin, but she was almost like a sister to Fran and Mouse. It was Mouse who did all the housekeeping and budgeting, and the supervision of the cooking, but it was my aunt Louisa who held the reins and the household revolved around her. And once the women left when the Japanese came, of course the men were all at sea.'

The light had almost gone while we were talking, the nights still drawing in early. I was anxious to get back to London and have some of the evening to myself before facing my class of kids in the morning.

Just before I left, my father got up suddenly and said, 'Wait a minute, Chrissie. I nearly forgot.' He turned on the Chinese lamp on the bureau and carefully opened the top drawer. 'I've found something that you might find interesting,' he called over his shoulder. Picking up a bulky-looking envelope, he pulled out some faded-blue, typewritten papers, stapled together. 'It looks like some papers belonging to Lion,' he said, peering at them. 'Laura must have typed them; she was the one who did all the typing in the house.'

I took them and flicked over a few leaves. It was a diary.

'I probably had this for years, Chrissie. Never thought about it. Tell you the truth, I don't remember when it was given to me. See if it will have what you want.'

5

LION

February 1942

Lion seems to have started his diary in response to the shock of the fall of Singapore. Bobby had told me about his time in Pegu with Lion, just before the town was evacuated. He'd shown me a photo of Lion, probably taken the year before, standing awkwardly in front of his government house. Lion was in a stiff, white judicial collar and a short black jacket – a balding, serious-looking man in his late forties. As I scanned through the flimsy pages, the news was grim on all sides. Lion's entries were testy, nervous. Perhaps, it seemed to me, he was struggling to maintain a sense of his own importance in the face of official directives and counter-directives. Above all, perhaps, like all his colleagues and acquaintances who teemed through his diary pages, he was just trying to survive the chaos.

Chrissie S.

LB Hennessy – his diary

Sunday, 15 February, Pegu

Singapore has fallen. The news is too dire and dark to be taken in fully. It must have stunned everyone in Burma, although actually the news couldn't have been altogether unexpected to anyone with any awareness.

Thursday, 19 February, Pegu and Rangoon

I was in Pegu on Monday, which had a short air raid in the afternoon. It's more alarming now since we know that the Japs are free to turn their full attention here to us after the fall of Singapore. Bobby arrived from Prome and Rangoon in good spirits. It seems the boy has no idea of the sort of mess that we're in.

On Tuesday I went to Rangoon and back. It is quite absurd to stay in Pegu when it's going to fall any day. It's impossible to get any sense out of anyone. The road to Rangoon was deserted except for military vehicles.

Today was a truly awful day. I spent the morning trying to commandeer a bus or lorry and eventually got hold of a dilapidated jeep.

I went to Rangoon in the jeep. Before I left Pegu, Collings of the US army told me that it was a matter of hours before it would be attacked, and the thought didn't make me feel at all comfortable on my journey. The road was entirely militarised. There was an ominous stillness, the villages empty with not even pi-dogs around. There is a curious metallic readiness for events. The Japs are near Bilin, and Pegu is distinctly in the danger zone now.

I saw the stationmaster at Pegu about sorting out accommodation on the train for the servants so that they can get away. The authorities have made no arrangement for evacuating Pegu. I phoned the commanding officer at HQ from the station and was met with the brusque reply that nothing could be done as Rangoon had to be served first. The stationmaster was not to be allowed to utilise a single truck at Pegu. Yet Pegu is much more in the affected area and will be the next district headquarters to go.

Collings told me the Chinese lorries have stopped using the Rangoon-Pegu-Mandalay Road from today and were going up the Prome Road instead. It seems that lorries and petrol dumps on the trunk road are being burned to prevent them from falling into enemy hands.

I came back from Rangoon dead beat and depressed.

Friday, 20 February, Pegu and leave for Upper Burma
I had a busy morning moving out of the house and evacuating. I made arrangements for the servants to go by train and am much indebted to the stationmaster. I had last minute office work and other business. I returned 5,000 rupees to the Treasury.

65

I left Pegu at 1.40 in the afternoon, taking Murthi with me in the jeep. We were not allowed to enter Rangoon, so we went up the Prome Road to Tharrawaddy for the night.

Saturday, 21 February, Prome

I left for Prome at about 10 o'clock after breakfast and arrived first thing in the afternoon, finding Robert there. Prome is full of cholera, and it seems certain that Rangoon will soon be evacuated. Robert gave me news from Calcutta, where it seems that all is well and the girls are settling in. Bea and family are now safely in Maymyo.

I tried to persuade Robert to come with me in the car, but he stayed back because of some business he expected to do. I left Prome for Maymyo after tea and arrived there at dusk. At first a police inspector tried to stop me from entering the town following orders that all cars were to be stopped because of the congestion on the road to Yenangyaung.

Wednesday, 25 February, Mandalay

I left Maymyo on Sunday after I'd managed to wangle five gallons of petrol, although of course petrol is not being sold to civilians. At Yenangyaung I bought a tin of salmon and some Chinese biscuits which turned out to be bad. I filled up with petrol and then went on to Gwegyo, a delightful drive through pleasant country. However, once there, I spent the night in a filthy *dak* bungalow.

The following day I left at about 9 o'clock in the morning. It was difficult going in parts, but a beautiful drive. I bought some stores at Meiktila. There were only three gallons of petrol allowed for each car, but fortunately the petrol dump controller knew me – he had heard me lecturing. I arrived in Mandalay at sixish and found the servants safe.

There were three air-raid alarms today.

Thursday, 26 February, Mandalay

I stayed at Tun Tin's last night. Both host and hostess are charming. Mrs Tun Tin provided an English dinner for me because she thought I wouldn't enjoy Burmese food, and she and her husband had it with me, although I'm sure they didn't care at all for European food. I actually preferred the Burmese food they gave me – she was quite mistaken in thinking that I wouldn't or didn't enjoy it.

I'm trying to find out my instructions. It's being suggested that I should go to Shwebo as District and Sessions Judge. I'm not keen. How on earth can I settle down to writing judgements now and send people to prison who are going to be let out again as soon as the district becomes a war-affected area? Hendriks suggests that he and I go to Maymyo ourselves to see about getting executive jobs. His idea of an executive post is a safe one in connection with evacuation in some way, and directly in the line of exit to India. And so is mine! He doesn't think Shwebo is safe because it's a rebellious district, and he's worried there could be some internal trouble which could be worse than having the Japanese invade the place, or at least as bad!

Friday, 27 February, Mandalay

Manley came over in the afternoon and we had a long chat in my bedroom. He told me about the Myitkyina route north-eastwards into India. It's difficult terrain and almost impossible to pass through once the monsoon breaks. He tried to persuade me to go out for drinks but I knew what that would lead to, so I declined.

So many people seem to be quite oblivious to the fact that all of us have had to come away from our homes, leaving everything behind, and that we've all had to endure all sorts of discomforts and so on. I know all that's nothing to what thousands of poor people have had to survive in Rangoon and other evacuated towns. And the fate of the wretched coolies and the people, quite mad, who have been turned out of the asylum – all let down by the government and left to fend for themselves in a doomed city.

The days are all too short and I seem to get nothing done. There were two air alarms today, but no sign of any bombers.

I left for Maymyo at 11.30, taking the chief clerk with me, and we arrived just after lunch. I had a job finding Dunkley and then he didn't seem pleased to see me. He stood on the steps and exclaimed, 'Well, Mr Hennessey?' The pompous, ill-bred fellow. He changed when I told him that I had brought up some of his stuff, and asked me if I'd had anything to eat. I told him that I had no wish to be appointed to Shwebo and that my idea was to try and get an executive job. He said that everybody wanted an executive job, including himself. I replied that he was all right as he was the Chief Justice now. Mrs Dunkley came to the steps and was profuse in her thanks for bringing up her parcels. She then talked non-stop for fifteen minutes while I tried to get away. That woman bores me stiff. The secret of her repulsiveness, I think, is her sublime self-centredness.

Later I had a long chat with the Attorney General and talked too much, the very thing that I accuse Mrs Dunkley of. I, I, I, me, me, me. Pah!

At 5.30 I left for Mandalay and found Ghose waiting for me when I arrived at Tun Tin's house. I listened to his tale of woe about my indebtedness to him, which he seems to have blathered out to everyone. I then went on up to the Mandalay railway station to meet Robert, who had left a chit for me at Tun Tin's. Thank goodness he got here safely. He came in the Ford – good old car. I took Robert over to Aungbale where I have rented some rooms for 35 rupees a month.

Hendriks had left a message at Tun Tin's that he wanted to see me urgently. Given my experience of those I've been meeting in the last few weeks, I knew at once that it would be about some urgent business of his rather than anything to do with me. And sure enough it was. He wanted me to cash his advance salary cheque and his chit for the price of his car out of the government funds that I had in my possession.

I paid off the cook with a bit extra. He is to go on the train tonight with his family; the train will be leaving early in the morning.

A telegram arrived from Laura. It had been sent on 24 February and said, 'Arrived safely Tamu. Very fit. Fondest love, Laura.'

Monday, 2 March, Mandalay

Hendriks called yesterday while the Tun Tins and I were at breakfast. He tried to preach optimism to us, but all the while having a most pessimistic air. It seemed as if he was trying to convince himself that everything was all right and that all would end well.

The convoy for India left at about 10 o'clock in the morning. I saw them off, including the Hendriks. They were all third-class carriages – real refugee scenes. No Indians were allowed.

I had news that Bobby is here in Mandalay – so that accounts for the whole family now. Harry has gone to Twantewa to bring up some Irrawaddy boats, but his destination is Prome or Upper Burma. Thank heavens none of our lot is trapped down in Rangoon.

I sat up until past 11 o'clock chatting to Robert about the route out of Burma through the Hukawng Valley to Assam. We are seeing people leaving in their droves every day, so it's inevitable that the talk everywhere is nothing but evacuation.

We had one air raid alarm today about 3 o'clock but we didn't bother about it.

6

CHRISSIE

February 1986

I hung the print of the Shwedagon Pagoda – the one found in Laura's boxes – on the wall of the narrow hallway of my flat. The lines were faint, but I could see that the proportions of the pagoda were striking, the human figures almost insignificant against a grand stairway, guarded by two enormous gilded lion-like creatures. I tried to imagine the Shwedagon as Bobby had driven into the ravaged streets of Rangoon at the end of January 1942, untouched among the devastation – the Japanese holding back from bombing such an important and holy place.

I was able to get a pass to study in the Senate House library in Bloomsbury, and went searching for books on Burma. As I walked towards the entrance I looked up at the glorious art deco tower with its cream-coloured stone, a modern temple, I thought, also surviving destruction from bombs in the Blitz. I climbed up to one of the upper floors with the stacks on Asia, and found a volume by a Victorian traveller, with fabulous coloured prints. The Shwedagon looked magnificent, with its golden *stupa* and diamonds at the top of the spire, and its shimmering walls. The flights of covered stairs and great terraces, I read, would be bustling with pilgrims and decked with shrines and stalls selling flowers, offerings, images of the Buddha and souvenirs. The lion creatures were the *chinthe*, beasts of legend and Buddhist mythology, and guardians of the temples and royal palaces.

I looked for pictures of Mandalay, the famed walled city founded by King Mindon on the banks of the Irrawaddy. We had read Kipling's poems at school – his verses telling of wind in the palm trees and temple bells; the refrain 'Come you back to Mandalay!' had been beating in my head. I found coloured prints and old photographs of the golden palace with its moat and the mass of pagodas with their *stupas* on Mandalay Hill. I read how King Thibaw and his wife, the Queen Supayalat, had lost Mandalay to the British, their story notorious for the wealth and splendour that was combined with wild excesses and pitiless human slaughter.

*

I arrived home at the end of a school day in the second week of February, running through the front door to silence the ringing phone. It was Jo-Jo. She wanted to know how my father was, and then we chatted for a while about the miserable weather and my lack of a boyfriend.

She said, 'The reason I phoned, darling, was to say why don't you come down at the weekend for a meal. We've found some more papers that I think you might be interested in.'

I was more than interested. That Sunday I headed to south London, arriving at Jo-Jo's just before lunch.

'I'm intrigued.' I said, still taking my coat off.

Jo-Jo went to sort out drinks and Richard disappeared upstairs, calling out, 'Give me a few minutes, Chrissie. I've put them somewhere safe.'

He came back with a tattered brown envelope-style folder. 'We found some more bits and pieces and thought we'd better check carefully after you discovered the letters last time. Jo-Jo says it looks like something Laura was writing.'

I opened the folder and pulled out a pile of papers. They were held together with a cord through a hole punched into the top left-hand corner. It looked a mess: typed pages, pages struck through, additions in pencil and passages written in a cramped hand. While my aunt was getting lunch ready I quickly leafed through. It seemed Laura had been determined to write up her escape from Rangoon in the last days before the final evacuation, and the story of her trek to safety across the mountains.

Underneath the sheaf of pages, I found separate typed notes, headed up, 'Burma to India: River steamers/overland route.' It detailed the route by river on steamers leaving from Prome –

71

an eleven-day journey up the Irrawaddy and Chindwin rivers, finally arriving at Sittaung. From there the overland trek was through Tamu on the Burma-India border and then to Imphal, the capital of Manipur State. I knew from evenings with an atlas, after my chats with my father, that the route across the border between the two countries covered a high mountainous region.

I called out, waving the piece of paper, 'Wow, this seems to be the itinerary that Laura used. This must've been something she got together before setting out.'

'Well, you can take it all back with you later, Chrissie.'

Jo-Jo was setting things out for lunch and, I thought, wanted me to put the folder away.

*

From my long afternoons with my father, a faintest outline had begun to emerge of my grandfather, Robert, together with Lion and the women, as they had been in those years when the war convulsed their world and changed things so definitively. I found a copy of George Orwell's *Burmese Days*, and images of snipe shooting in the early morning mists, up-country bazaars and drunken evenings in the club were haunting me. I was anxious to hear what Jo-Jo remembered about her childhood.

That afternoon she started telling me about an almost Victorian childhood, with strict discipline imposed by the family members who surrounded them. But for Jo-Jo there was always escape to the servants' quarters where she squatted, a little girl speaking Burmese, Hindustani and a smattering of Tamil, listening to tales of Brahma and Vishnu, who were always painted in blue to depict their infinite divinity. And there were thrilling stories about Shiva, and about the monkey god, Hanuman, and Ravana, the demon king.

'We had so many visitors and wonderful parties,' Jo-Jo told me. Somerset Maugham had stayed in the 1920s, she said, when Fran and Mouse were still young, and he was already a well-known writer. And Lion, it seemed, knew everyone, from Orwell himself to the royal princesses. There was even a story of how her father, Robert, had been taken to the royal palace at Mandalay as a baby, a few years before King Thibaw's exile to India, and been given a magnificent ruby and a solid golden bowl as presents.

'What happened to them – the presents?' I asked.

'Lost, with everything else. Lost . . .'

Jo-Jo lit a cigarette. 'If you can imagine it, darling,' she said, 'our house was right on the lake, with steps from the garden that went down to the water's edge. We were on a sort of promontory, so you could see the lake from three-quarters of the house.'

'Did you go out on it?'

'Good Lord, yes. We had three or four boats. I remember there was a dinghy with a sail, which Bobby was always messing about in. There were islands on the lake all dotted around, and sometimes my father would decide to have dinner out on one of them. So, before the meal the servants used to go across in the boats, with all the silver and buckets of ice, and lay the food out on a large white tablecloth and then, when it was ready, we would all go over and have the most gorgeous picnics.'

I smiled. I thought about my father and how he always loved water, and listening for bird call on hot summer evenings. Jo-Jo tapped lightly on her cigarette, so that tiny particles of ash detached themselves and floated down onto the agate ashtray.

Jo-Jo's stories of Kokine now sat alongside Orwell's Burma, an improbably romantic portrayal: the chink of glasses as *chota pegs* were taken on the lawn of the large house by the lake in the clear, translucent evening light; the outline of palm trees faintly edged against a lemon-tinted sky. A life of empire that was soon to be swept away.

7

LAURA

February 1942

I wanted to breathe in the stillness of our garden for the last time, as if in that way I could hold on to the moment. The sky was showing signs of early dawn and my beloved trees – the mangoes, palms, tamarind and neem – were shrouded in opal light, their shapes brocaded against the sky.

I pulled my gaze back to the small pile of luggage stacked neatly against the car, an almost indistinct shape in the faint morning light. There wasn't much of it: a couple of pieces of soft luggage, rolls of bedding and mosquito nets, a gun case converted into a stores box with food supplies, tea and dried milk, water bottles, and cans of petrol that Harry had managed to collect the previous day. I had tried to be strict with the amount I packed but, foolishly, Harry said, I'd stuffed the sides and corners of my bag with my sketch pad and pastels, some mementos and family photos, and had sewn jewellery into my clothes.

'Talk about burning your boats,' I said aloud and then muttered, 'Let's get on with it,' in a feeble attempt to lift my spirits and show the sort of determination I knew we needed. Since my aunt Louisa left for Calcutta we'd been staying at the Hut with Robert. We had left the dog with Robert until Harry could get back to collect him and I hadn't been able to pick myself up since. The servants had been anxious to leave since the end of January and Harry had paid all of them off except the driver. Robert had asked us to take Appaswamy, the butler, with us to join the Family in Calcutta. Appaswamy was still quite young, unmarried, and was Aunt Louisa's right-hand man. He was now settling an untidy bundle with some cooking pots on top of the other luggage. I had wanted to spend the last night at home. It had turned out to be a mistake – the house had been empty and desolate, and I felt an enormous sadness as we packed the car, leaving only one man to guard the place. It was like leaving a loved one.

I couldn't help feeling defeated to be accepting the general mood of panic and joining the demoralised crowds that had been scrambling out of Rangoon since the Christmas bombing. Now it was clear that the enemy was pushing into Upper Burma; the tide was surging north again and this time there was no turning back.

'We're off, Laura!'

Harry was helping the driver to strap the last of the luggage onto the car. I couldn't say anything, so I climbed in and, once we had swung through our gates and out to the road, I concentrated on the shadows cast by the heavy trees on either side. The Prome Road was a broad, grey ribbon before us, already pulsing with people, trucks and carts. My throat ached and I could feel the echo of the nightly warning sirens ringing in my ears. I hadn't been able to eat since lunch the day before; now I felt slightly sick and held my arms across the top of my stomach. Yet I felt strangely detached from the greyness of the dawn and the swelling crowd of evacuees.

The morning air was still cool. I wrapped my shawl closer and looked across at Harry. Five years before, when we were first married, I used to stare at him in a sort of wonder that he was my husband. He had an ease about him, a carelessness. I didn't realise then that this was a barrier he threw around himself, detaching him from the rest of us. I looked away and out of the window, focusing on nothing in particular.

Most of the European families had been getting out by air and sea since the bombing started, but this had become increasingly difficult. I was meeting up with Vera Langham and her two little boys to make the trek through the mountains, from Sittaung on the Chindwin River to Tamu and then through the Naga Hills into Manipur. I was grateful that Harry could come with me as far as Monwya, and after that we would be relying on the porters to be our guides. They would also provide protection against the *dacoits* that were becoming an ever-increasing menace, attacking groups of refugees.

We had heard that the numbers of evacuees were beginning to build up on the different routes into Tamu. Forestry workers had been setting up camps along the way, and we hoped to be able to cover the distance between them every day easily enough. It didn't sound too bad, but Robert said that we shouldn't be deceived: the route was mountainous and would involve some steep climbs.

'Why don't you sleep, Laura?' Harry's voice seemed to reach me from a distance.

I didn't reply. Shapes were becoming clearer in the early morning light, and we were soon surrounded by crowds streaming on either side of us, ghostly vehicles and open carts piled with belongings, evacuees wrapped in scarves and muffled against the morning chill, carrying small children and bundles stacked on their heads. As the road became more active, it was impossible to block out the hooting of the horns. At one point, I started forward as the car stopped suddenly behind a block of enormous trucks driving in close formation, and a cloud of dust enveloped us. Once the dust subsided, Appaswamy leant out of the window from his seat in the front and shouted as the driver pulled out and joined the traffic again.

We were moving slowly with bullock carts, rickshaws and motorised vehicles blocking the road. It seemed that animals and humans were part of a single surge forward, here and there broken trucks left abandoned on the side of the road. Then, as we got into the open countryside, a stream of refugees marched beside the flat, parched paddy fields as though extras in a silent film. I felt more awake and thought: I should be remembering this. I tried to focus on the details of the countryside – a flock of ducks rasping and flapping their wings at the side of the road alongside us at Pyuntaza, the flat roof and sound of the steam engine in a rice mill at Peinzalok, as if life were unchanged, and then Indian huts among the hills and palms when we reached Yedashe, north of Toungoo. We passed the teak forests, the tall slender trunks with doomed white circles at Swa, a sawmill with its mounds of logs, and then a village of stork-like huts with an offering to the *nats*, the spirit gods of Burma.

From Pyuntaza, most of the way we followed the railway line that ran north from Moulmein, and from time to time we would cross it or run side by side with trains carrying refugees north in open compartments, like cattle trucks. It was early evening before we approached Meiktila, our first stop. In Rangoon, our company car had been commandeered and the old Austin that Harry had managed to get hold of the previous week was coping poorly with the rough road, bumping and lurching in the ruts made by carts and heavy lorries.

As we drove in to Meiktila, there was an increasing number of wayside sellers sitting under umbrellas, selling small fans, cool drinks and green coconuts, which they split with *dahs*. Small children ran to the open windows with their offerings. We were met by a barrage of sound as the sellers competed for custom against the sound of vehicles and the screaming of bullock cart wheels. We drove into the town slowly, the car spluttering and jerking forward.

*

As the light faded in the late afternoon, I was lying on the bed in the *dak* bungalow, a basic brick and timber affair with a pervasive smell of bats, staring at the chinks of light showing through the roof. Harry came in and tossed his jacket onto the bed.

'We'll take a taxi tomorrow, Laura. The man will get the car to Mandalay and sort it out.'

He raised the mosquito netting and sat on the bed. He stared down at me and lifted some hair off my face, brushing my cheek with the palm of his hand.

'I shall miss you, Laura,' he said. His other hand was moving over my thigh and he leant over and kissed me gently. His lips moved down to my breast, nudging aside the neck of my dress.

'Don't Harry, I'm tired and hot. Not now.'

I turned slightly, pulling myself up on one elbow, so that his head was pushed away. He looked round at me without saying anything, and then suddenly got up. I waited until I heard the door shut smartly.

I looked through the netting at the bare eaves of the bungalow. A mosquito was whining, circling the space above the bed, and I could hear the loud scratching and the calls of birds on the roof. Beyond, there was the never-ceasing noise of heavy lorries and car horns.

I closed my eyes. I remembered a glorious sunset the first time we visited Kalaw together, in the Shan hills; it was a few weeks after we got married. We stood on the hotel balcony and watched the sky darken in mauves and pinks. 'This is the start of a new life for you, Laura.' Harry had pulled me towards him so that I was pressed hard against his jacket. 'For both of us, Harry,' I'd said.

It had been about this time of year that Harry and I married, in the spring of 1937. He had been one of Fran's tennis partners many years before, in the days when Fran was still the girl about town. She had a pack of admirers, but she and Harry came together over their passion for tennis. Since that time we'd bumped into him at parties, but then I got to know him better in the summer of 1936 while on holiday in our house in Pagoda Point, on the coast. He came to play bridge and join our play-reading evenings. I knew that he had fallen down the social list, but he was still smart and attractive, and I was flattered by his attention. For my part, I was no longer expecting marriage. Even on my wedding day I was still in a state of mild disbelief.

*

The next morning I woke up without the taut emotions of the day before. I had a slight flash of anticipation. At Mandalay we were to meet up with Vera and her two children, and then the journey would be properly underway. Her husband, Peter, had been a friend of Harry's for years. Vera was someone who lived in perpetual fear of the drinking water and the food, and her nervousness of the sometimes unpredictable world Peter drew her into had only increased with motherhood. Despite it all, I liked her well enough.

Once on the road, the chaos was even greater than the previous day, with crowds of refugees on foot and vehicles of all descriptions performing an elaborate dance around each other to a soundtrack of calls and shouts, and brakes screeching. Our driver seemed to be attempting to prove his own driving skills against those of others on the road and we couldn't help but join in the effort, issuing warnings and directions from our huddled position in the back. It was exhausting. The dust hung like vapour in the dry heat and from time to time we stopped at little wayside stalls, which were doing a roaring trade brewing up tea on open fires.

Mandalay sat on the Irrawaddy River. It was once the Gem City, housing the palace of the Burmese royal family, and was still known for its fort and its moat, but it was a straggling, dusty town. We arrived in mid-afternoon, with the heat burning in my nostrils and my blouse clinging to my back. I was sticky with dust and could smell the faint odour of my own sweat; my feet moved uncomfortably against the damp soles of my sandals. We were stopping overnight in a large government rest house, a single-roofed, two-storied wooden bungalow and, as the car pulled up, I peered out of the window in relief. Harry got out first, stretching and easing his back, and then came round to my side of the car to help me out.

It was quiet when we pulled our luggage into the passageway. The dining room on the lower floor was open and cool, and I wandered through it onto a cemented veranda, feeling a welcome stillness. Harry went back to help Appaswamy bring things from the taxi, so I decided to carry on upstairs. The staircase was protected by a batten-trellised screen and led to a large room; there was a scruffy-looking register on a heavy table and an inkpot and pen next to it. Looking around, I could see piles of luggage stacked in different corners. The room contained a few straight-backed cane-bottomed chairs and also some more comfortable chairs with leg rests that would have allowed you to stretch out in easier times. They looked like bliss after our cramped journey in the taxi.

An elegant Burmese woman, her hair heavy with coconut oil and coiled in a massive cylinder on top of her head, walked over to one of the windows and looked away as I came in. She must have heard my footsteps clattering on the worn wood of the stairs. I thought her eyes looked swollen and wondered for a moment about her own story and if she was also moving up-country. I felt an urge to excuse myself for leaving – for deserting in the face of danger. For a moment I could imagine pulling her round and saying, 'Don't judge me. I never wanted to leave but what else can we do?'

'Hello, Laura! Lovely to see you, my dear.' Peter almost bounced into the room, a heavy man with black, wiry hair and a thick moustache. 'I saw Harry by the car. How did he get away?'

'He managed to get a few days of leave. And he has business up-country anyway, so it worked out.' I tried to sound bright.

'Well, delighted you girls will have a man with you, at least until Mawlaik.' He called out, 'Vera, they're here!'

'Darling!' Vera rushed out of one of the rooms and kissed me. She looked ready for an afternoon tea party in a fashionably short floral dress, pulled in tightly at the waist and with puffed sleeves. She had one of those creamy, silky complexions that I always envied; she was looking even paler than usual and had rouged her cheeks heavily.

'I'm so sorry – I didn't hear you come up,' Vera said. 'I've got the two boys in the bathroom at the moment.' On cue there were insistent calls from along the corridor and she fled.

Peter laughed. 'My son, Ben, is a very persistent young man.'

*

The next morning the Monywa train moved slowly out of Mandalay, so full that there was barely breathing room, and I felt slightly faint from the heat and the stench that had followed us from the heaving platform and into the carriage. This is only the beginning, I thought. As we pulled away I tried to distract myself and idly watched a group of young monks on the other side of the track, conspicuous in their saffron-coloured robes and with their shaven heads. The crowds at the station had been appalling and getting on board was chaotic, with a confusion of people, crying children, boxes, bags, and unwieldy packages and bundles. Harry had been forced to get on further up the train with Appaswamy, leaving Vera and me with the boys in the packed carriage. Tommy, at six years old, was a rather serious child, with dark hair falling in a heavy fringe across his forehead and a gap where his front teeth were missing. He had been adored and petted by his mother until he was upstaged by Ben's arrival.

Vera was now dozing opposite me. Tommy's comics had fallen to the floor and he kicked his legs gently while he listened to a story being told by a young subaltern, who was making a good job of entertaining them both. Ben was curled up against me, sucking his thumb vigorously and gazing unblinkingly at the soldier. He had round spectacles set on still chubby cheeks; they gave him the appearance of a little owl, and his body felt warm and comforting. I could hardly believe that we were in the middle of a tragedy. Yet our lives were now broken, fragmented. For a moment I wondered if the young man in front of us would still be alive in two or three months' time, and then I wanted to take back the thought, as if I had brought him bad luck. I looked over at him and smiled.

I thought about my cousin, Bobby. He was exposed, travelling about from one telegraph centre to another, although I knew he was usually well ahead of the Japanese advance. But the villages had become less and less secure over the last few months, with reports of *dacoity* and murderous attacks, virtually unchecked. I was fond of Bobby. I was nearly twenty years older than him, and my cousins and I had looked after him on and off, together with his sisters, after his mother died and he had come to join the Family at Kokine in our house by the Victoria Lakes. Bobby had become an attractive, sensitive young man, lacking in confidence, I always thought, although he seemed happy enough with the work he was doing with the Signals.

Tommy stopped kicking his legs and I looked over my arm to see if he had fallen asleep. He was listening hard to the young soldier.

'And as the Japs crept in single file under the tree we jumped on their backs and gave them . . .'

'A nelson!' Tommy cried out.

The soldier looked surprised.

'Yes,' he said, 'and we tied every one of them into a knot – a reef knot – and then we tied them all together with an enormous granny knot.'

'How many were there?' Tommy persisted.

'Oh, dozens of them – maybe even a hundred.' The soldier grinned across at me.

'Phew!' said Tommy, bending down to pick up his comic. 'It's jolly lucky you were up in the tree and could jump on them.'

The young soldier suddenly pulled Tommy towards the window and said, 'Look at that bird! I once had a bird like that. It built a nest in my hair – just here!' He pointed to his well-brushed hair, fixed smooth to his head with Brylcreem, and then he ruffled it so that spikes stood up in all directions. Ben leant his head back against me as he giggled, and I suddenly felt more relaxed.

The train slowly cut through the country. The back of the wooden seat was uncomfortable against my spine and I thought about a small pillow that I had packed into our baggage somewhere. I turned my face up towards the tiny fan in the ceiling of the compartment but it didn't offer up even the slightest air current. Leaning my cheek against the window, I gazed at the open, monotonous countryside of millet, paddy and wheat fields.

Our rail journey was ending in the early hours at Monywa, a port on the Chindwin River. We were planning to start our four-day river journey the following day and would be due to arrive at Mawlaik on Saturday. Harry was going to leave us there, but we had a further day's journey upriver to Sittaung, where our march would begin.

When we arrived at Monywa, we found a desperate crowd spilling out of the little shack that was the booking office. People were packed solidly inside a fenced-in enclosure, clambering in and out of the booking office windows in the hope of getting some of the limited number of tickets available.

'Memsahib, please do something for us.' An old Indian held on to my arm as we pushed our way through the crowd. 'We have been waiting here for very many days. The boats are coming and going, but until now they are not giving us tickets. Soon we will have no money to get them as we have to buy food also.'

I couldn't move any further through the crowd and I turned to look at him. 'My daughter also,' he said, 'she is having her baby soon and if she doesn't go now she will be too heavy to walk.'

I looked at him blankly. Harry turned back to me, his head high above the swell of evacuees. 'Laura, come on!' He was gesturing at me and I suddenly panicked. There was some movement in the crowd as a sense ran through it that I was a possible source of help. Hands began pulling at my dress and tapping on my shoulder.

'Memsahib, you must help.' The old man was still tugging at my arm.

I was suddenly swept by a powerful sense of self-preservation and pushed through, catching up with Harry. I held on to his elbow, feeling cold and unhappy inside. I couldn't think about it. I wanted to get on the boat.

*

An hour later, our steamer was progressing slowly up the Chindwin River, its great paddle wheels pounding the water. The crowd on the bank receded slowly into the distance and the golden pagoda faded into the early morning mists. It was a traditional two-deck steamer, with two hundred or more third-class passengers – mostly Indians as far as I could see – packed onto the lower deck. We were more of a mixed group on our small saloon deck, but every chair and table was occupied. There were baskets and bundles stacked into corners and wedged between people, and clothes hung to dry from the overhead tarpaulin. Children sat on suitcases and on the floor among piles of gourds and coconuts. Many of the women were clutching *tiffin* carriers and tin basins containing food, and had packages wrapped into the hems of loose blouses or the folds of saris. From time to time a child's loud wail would set off others. Around us there was some intermittent chattering as women talked of their plans, such as they were. Some of them were intending to leave the river at Mawlaik and join roughly-organised parties of women and children who were leaving on elephants along a rough mountainous track to Tamu. Others were planning to follow the same route as us on foot along the shorter hilly path from Sittaung. There were just a few men – most, like Appaswamy, family servants travelling on the lower deck. Harry was conspicuous, and I could see that he felt uncomfortable. It's okay, I wanted to say, he won't take up valuable space in the evacuation camps; he's essential personnel with business to do.

Later, camp cots were erected in neat rows across the deck and mosquito nets hung from an overhead mesh of string. Vera and I had arranged a field bed of mattresses and rugs on the small front deck and slung over it pale pink mosquito netting which I remembered used to cling to the walls of Vera's morning room. It already seemed a lifetime ago.

There was a queue all evening outside the only bathroom and toilet on the deck, but we finally managed to stake our claim. Harry was the last of our group to go in and I looked up as he came out, his scarlet dressing gown catching the glow of the overhead light, looking improperly smart.

'Right, I'm coming over,' he said. 'I'll sleep by the boys,' and he threaded his way between the cots.

Vera and I sat on deck propping ourselves up at the side of the boat, staring out at the darkness of the river and the shadowy banks. I got up first and pulled her up after me. 'Tomorrow will be here soon enough. Let's get some sleep.'

The next day was monotonous and wearying with the clamour on board. Vera and I spent most of the day sitting with the boys, waving as we passed villages set in clusters of overspreading trees. Women waved back to us as they bathed or washed clothes in the river, *longyis* hitched up under their armpits; children laughed and pointed, swam out to the boat or called out to us from the water's edge. But I felt tense. We weren't clear yet; it was easy to imagine Japanese snipers camouflaged in the jungle, which at times swept down to the river in thick green folds. I felt almost ready to hear the first shock of gun fire and it was only by talking that I could keep down the faint tide of nausea that had been with me since we'd left Rangoon. Vera and I exchanged stories about the evacuation and news of friends who had arrived safely in India. A bond quickly formed among the women on board and we chatted warmly to our fellow passengers. It seemed that most of the officials who had been urging us to stay put had suddenly discovered urgent business up-country or in India. It was now almost impossible to get tickets to leave by plane; many of us had found ourselves at the bottom of an impossibly long waiting list. The boat situation had become scandalous, space being taken up by luggage, including alcohol, while evacuees were being turned away. I poured out my worries about Robert and Lion and poor Bobby moving up and down the country through the war zone. Vera was hoping that we might have letters waiting for us at Tamu, but I thought it unlikely and told her about the reports of stacks of undelivered mail in the main post office.

We had a noisy arrival at Mingin. Voices were raised to combat the rattling of the chain cabling as it was lowered into the river. I was beginning to feel at ease, and we added to the general pandemonium as we constantly checked that we still had two children and all the necessary bits of luggage. Half a dozen men swam ashore with the cable, the fading light catching their bodies, and hauled the boat up to the shore. Then the deck passengers surged across the gangplanks that were swiftly thrown out. In a few minutes little camp fires were started and shadowy figures moved about in the glow. Soon, *betel* and *bedi* vendors were threading through the crowds and calling out, and eager buyers surrounded women selling beans, cucumbers, pumpkins and bundles of sugar cane. A woman walked down to the water's edge with a round bamboo holder of chickens, which was quickly commandeered by the ship's cook, together with several cylinders of eggs for the saloon kitchen. A sweet smell of jasmine swept across the deck as two young women, their cheeks whitened with *thanaka* paste, came on board with blossoms and hair garlands.

I watched the crowd on the shore together with other saloon passengers. It was improbably like a scene from a film, set against a backcloth of darkened palm trees and fragile huts, silhouetted against a pink-black sky. We were close enough to watch our travelling companions as they slipped into comforting evening routines. Little children were being bathed and oiled by the edge of the river, with a common bathing pool formed in the shallows between the boat and the shore. One woman, surrounded by children, the end of her sari pulled over her head, was baking a continuous stream of *chapatis*, stacking them and covering them with cloths in *tiffin* carriers for the next day. The chatter of human voices seemed to merge almost into a single sound, rising into the evening air at a slight distance from the boat, punctuated by the yelping of pariah dogs and the occasional cry of birds over the water. I could smell wood smoke, frying *chapatis* and the rich heavy odour of *ghee*. I suddenly felt hungry.

*

As I woke up the following morning, it became increasingly difficult to block out the murmur of voices on deck. The others had almost finished their breakfast by the time I went into the saloon, and Ben was standing on a chair in evident high spirits, waving a spoon in his hand. Yet dawn had hardly broken.

Fleecy, ruby-tinted clouds rose in crazy patterns across the sky, and the shore was bathed with an early light of the faintest pink.

'Sit down in your seat and say good morning to Auntie Laura, you little terror! And you, Tommy, have you finished your breakfast?'

Vera looked controlled, even business-like, and I smiled a greeting at the boys. Then we could hear a fever bird in a nearby jungle thicket crying piteously, 'Ko-ya! Ko-ya!' The nerve-racking call started on one note and gradually rose to a frenzied cry of distress.

'Poor Ko-ya,' I murmured. 'He's calling for his brother.'

'For his brother?' Ben looked up.

'It's an old Burmese story,' I explained. 'There were two brothers who were devoted to each other and one day the younger one got lost in a jungle, and the older brother beseeched the *nats* – you know, the spirits – to change him into a bird so that he could fly through all the jungles of Burma in search of him. The *nats* granted him his request, and now this little bird can be heard all over the country calling out to his brother.'

'Would you do that for your brother, Tommy?' Vera asked.

Ben stuck his tongue out at him and Tommy just said, 'He's silly,' and got up to join Harry, who was standing at the edge of the boat, looking over at the river bank.

I went to join my husband after breakfast. I thought that I should make an effort. Perhaps this time, this war – this disaster – could help to bring us back to the closeness we once had. I kept my shoulder against his arm and he looked down at me.

'You're on your way, Laura. You are on your way.'

Coming towards us, an oarsman was perched high in the delicately-carved stern of an old paddy boat – the great long boat used to carry rice – its sails and rigging down. He called out and one of the passengers, an Indian Chulia, replied in Burmese.

Vera came up. 'What was that about?'

'He wanted to know where we were going and our companion explained that the Japanese had burnt his house.' Then I added, 'I don't think he understood or believed him.' The two boats passed each other in silence. I shrugged. 'So many people in this country still don't know what's happening. I suppose we can't be surprised. I can hardly believe it myself.'

The strange feeling of unreality hit me again at the end of the day as we moved slowly into Kalemyo, welcomed by the glinting of kerosene lights on the shore. Little bells on the *htis* of the pagodas, hidden in jungle clearings, gave up a gentle sigh as they moved in the light evening breeze, the sound floating across the water. The Burmese craft settled down in the water like large crocodiles, their headlights glowing in the hazy twilight. I suddenly felt that I must get away from the boat. I wondered if it would be possible to have any news of Rangoon and the Japanese advance.

Harry put his arm around me. 'Come on, Laura, what's the point of chasing after bad news now?' he said, with a hint of irritation. 'You just have to stay focused.' I felt myself stiffening.

'Don't preach, please.' Harry's hand dropped from my shoulder.

I looked around. Vera was coming towards us, looking surprisingly cool. I waved and called to her. 'Harry will stay with the boys on board. Let's go and see what we can find out.'

*

After some discussion, the *serang*, an old-timer originally from Chittagong who had been on the river for thirty years, detailed one of the villagers – a young boy of about fifteen – to show us the way to the village. He set off a little ahead of us, his *longyi* tucked between his thighs, turning his head round to us from time to time and calling out encouragement into the dusk. Nevertheless, I began to wonder if we'd done the right thing; maybe there were fifth columnists in the village.

'How much further?' I asked, forcing a brightness to my voice, while kicking myself for not thinking, for taking the risk.

'Over there!' He pointed vaguely, sweeping with his hand beyond the immediate path and into the distance. Then the track suddenly turned and twisted between drab mat huts. The mud was baked hard by the sun, but I could smell the pools of fetid slush on either side. Chickens and ducks scattered as we approached and two or three pariah dogs yapped, somewhat without conviction, then dogged our heels. Most of the villagers were around the boat at the jetty, and the village was deserted except for the faint outline of a young girl with a baby at her hip, who disappeared quickly into a hut, then stood half-hidden in the darkened doorway, curious, as we passed by.

'Round the corner now,' said the boy in Burmese, swinging round and pointing to a house on stilts, railed in by a split bamboo fence. He unlatched the heavy wooden gate and we were met by hysterical barking from the back of the house, followed by a woman's vehement response.

'That's her!' the boy said.

We picked our way carefully up the wooden steps, which felt dangerously unstable and rotten in places. As I reached the narrow veranda, a middle-aged woman flung aside the bead curtain and stepped out of the room behind, framed in a faint yellow light. She stared at us, then lifted her gaze to look beyond, perhaps to check if there were any others. Her hair was untidily coiled at the back of her neck, encircled by strings of starflowers. Her face was smeared with *thanaka* paste and there were streaks lining the folds of her neck. She looked at Vera and me for a while, then pulled the curtain back and nodded towards the interior.

'Come in!'

Still hesitating on the veranda, I said, 'We heard you have a radio and we would very much like to hear the latest news. We've been out of touch with things for a few days.'

'Come in, come, please,' she repeated. 'It is about time for the news.' The cascade of green, blue and gold curtain swished behind us as we were shepherded into the inner room. There was a hurricane lamp burning dimly on one side of the room, encircled by a furious mass of insects that battered against it and spiralled upwards. The floor was stained by *betel* juice and covered by two worn mats. Looking around, I saw an ancient sewing machine against a wall. There was a pungent smell of clove and aniseed coming from a small table containing a tray with a lacquered box and a saucer of spices and lime paste. Underneath was a pile of fresh green leaves.

'Sit down, please.'

Vera sat on an ancient cane chair while I followed our hostess further into the room. She found the radio switch over in a corner, squatting down, her bangles clattering.

'There,' she proclaimed as an overloud, crackling sound burst out from the set. She turned to me suddenly, pulling herself up with her hand on her back. 'So, why are you leaving Burma? Are the British not going to fight?'

The question took me aback and it was Vera who answered, her voice thin and raised slightly.

'Yes, only the women and children are being sent out until the trouble is over.'

'But even the men are retreating.' It was a statement. The woman seemed determined not to give us any quarter. 'Of course they do not say this on the radio, but it is so. We see it.'

'They'll make a stand,' I said, feeling irritated, but I didn't know if I believed it. We were quitting – in the end it would be all of us. This woman could see the endgame.

'When will this stand happen?' She clicked her tongue against her teeth. Then she said, 'My son is in Maymyo, in the army,' and the mood lightened a little.

'You know,' she continued, 'you should have let us prepare for this defence of Burma if you did not intend to do it yourselves.'

She looked at me directly for a moment. Then, switching off the wireless, she said, 'Tsk, these atmospherics. Every day they disturb the news, but perhaps it is as well that they do.' She turned to me, shrugging her shoulders and spreading her hands. 'Yes, we should have defended Burma. We are not afraid.' Then, suddenly she said, 'Will you smoke? Will you have some sherbet ice?'

'Thank you, no,' Vera replied, getting up from the cane chair, as my own undecided response hung in the air. The woman must have understood her look of restrained offence. 'We must be going,' Vera added. 'We have little ones on board the boat.'

We moved to the door without saying anything else – it seemed to me, even greater strangers than when we came in. Yet this woman had stirred emotions, questions in my head that had been oppressing me since the journey on the Prome Road. The old order of things had been challenged; now everything was changing.

The young boy was waiting for us. We walked in silence back along the path, nervous in the darkness and holding on to each other.

After a while, Vera said, 'We should have said something, don't you think? Not let her say all that. It seems disloyal.'

'Mmm . . . I don't know. She was just telling us what she felt.'

I didn't trust myself to say much more. I felt cornered, forced to see myself and the whole boat party as she did. And I was irritated. The woman must surely know what the Japanese would do to British and Anglo-Burmese families and to the Indians, and to anyone connected to the administration.

The steamer seemed almost an old friend when we reached it. I had lost my appetite and didn't join the others for dinner. I took my seat at the side of the boat again, staring down into the darkness of the river eddies and at the faint shapes of the country boats tied up to struts, emptied for the night of their crowds of evacuees. The little fires on the shore gradually died down as the third-class passengers came back and, as the bank disappeared into the dark of the night, it was silent except for the clear call of the *lascar* on duty. The purple shadows slowly deepened, and fronds of floating weeds stifled tiny currents and sent a dank smell into the chill night air. By the time I crept into bed, Vera was already asleep and I moved my bedding closer to her.

*

By the next day, passengers were beginning to fret at the slow progress of the boat, a high-pitched, uneven hum of women's voices rising from the lower deck. Then, suddenly, we came to a halt against a partially submerged sandbank, the paddle churning to no avail. The old *serang* – the head of the crew – lifted his little circular cap and scratched his head reflectively, then rubbed the back of his neck with his hand. There were one or two calls from our companions for the deck passengers to get out and push. People hung over the side of the boat and soon the cry was taken up: 'Make them push! Push! Push!'

Little boats and *sampans* with painted eyes swung alongside and took the third-class passengers ashore, while on our upper deck there was a buzz of anticipation. The *lascars* rowed swiftly upstream carrying the anchor in the bottom of the dinghy – the winch clattering and rattling – and then with a tremendous splash the anchor settled in the river bed, sending a huge spray over the men in the row boat. The men heaved, chanting loudly with each effort, and with a terrific shudder the boat dragged on the firmly embedded anchor. The second-in-command was at the bow shouting; the boat's winchmen yelled in reply and bent their backs so that their muscles were edged taut across their shoulders. The chain suddenly sprang out of its moorings and the boat stirred hesitatingly, then slithered forward into deeper water. The crowd cheered from the bank as she slowly headed for the anchor with the engines pounding.

Once we had picked up the passengers, at last we were on our way. I pulled a chair up to the rail and let the soft plash of the river against the side of the boat and the midday warmth soothe me.

*

'Auntie Laura! Kalewa!' Tommy woke me. 'It's half-past four and we're almost at Kalewa. Hurrah!' He was running around somewhere near me.

'And you've been asleep for a hundred years,' Ben said, patting my head. I was soon fully awake to the now familiar noise and bustle of the loading and unloading of firewood and passengers.

'Why have the people downstairs got their luggage ready?' Tommy was peering over the rail.

'Do we have to get off, too?' Ben joined Tommy.

'No,' I replied. 'We go to Sittaung further up the river. Those people have buses and camps along this road for them, and our trek starts from Sittaung where there are camps for us.'

'Birds of a feather flock together!' Tommy said in a sing-song voice.

'Tommy, what do you mean?'

'Our *chaprasi* taught me that.'

'Yes, I know the rhyme, Tommy.'

I was shocked that Tommy could so quickly apply the rules of our society to the chaos around us. But it was true. We were being segregated. And Harry had told me that the track the refugees would be joining could take bullock carts and elephants, but most of them would have to walk through thick jungle. It was proving treacherous; I had heard that hundreds of refugees were dying on the way – the Kabaw Valley was unhealthy and notorious for malaria. There was talk of a serious cholera outbreak affecting the camps, in the way the disease had taken hold in Prome. Many of the evacuees were already weak when they started as they had been struggling on the road from Lower Burma or waiting in refugee camps for transport, living on little more than rice and dal, and suffering from dysentery and other sickness.

'What nonsense is Tommy telling you?' Vera came up, and Ben ran to her and clung to her hands, swinging backwards and forwards.

'They are just keeping me entertained,' I said. 'I'd been dozing.' I didn't feel like giving an account of my exchange with her eldest son.

*

Once more, as darkness fell, the shoreline was distorted – as if a mirage – with shadows thrown across the water. I thought about the refugees that had left us and hoped they had found safety in their first evacuation camp. Kalewa had looked ramshackle and unappealing, and I was glad we were moving on.

The saloon boy came almost running, pushing through the passengers on the deck, balancing a plate of sticky cakes.

'Look, no cakes for supper. All spoilt with tongue.' He looked accusingly at the boys.

Vera turned Ben towards her and looked at him sternly. 'Ben, did you do that?'

'Only one lick,' he mumbled. What had been fine whirls of delicate icing were now sloppy smudges of cochineal and chocolate. Harry swept him up and proclaimed him the cake-licking champion. Ben cautiously started giggling, looking sideways at his mother, and then, in the general confusion of apologies and explanations, the tensions of the evening disappeared.

*

The next day the jungle swept down, relentless, to the water's edge. It was now six days since we had set out from Rangoon. The scenery was magnificent, and the outcrops of little isolated villages in squared fields of cultivation threw the wild surroundings into a sharper relief.

We watched, exhausted by the heat on deck, mere spectators in an everyday drama played out at the water's edge. A buffalo, lazily wallowing in the grey mud, a white pond heron on its back, another feeding on water hyacinth with a small boy sitting on its bony spine, waving a stick at us. A young girl with flowers in her hair, laying offerings at a riverside shrine. Simple bamboo stands with earthenware jars of drinking water put out for the *poongyis* – the monks. And everywhere there were white pagodas, their *htis*, like beautiful golden umbrellas, standing out against the grey sky. It sometimes seemed as if this whole panorama floated by while we stayed motionless.

The scenery was breathtaking, with high, jagged ridges falling sharply into the river on either side. Then, away in the distance, swathed by mists, we finally saw Mawlaik, a trading point and the headquarters of the district forestry office. Its thatched huts were faintly etched, leaning over the steep river bank.

The children were scrubbed and dressed, and Vera and I had dug into our bags to find fresh clothes. Vera had on dark blue slacks and a grey *moiré* shirt, looking incongruously smart. We could almost be mistaken for a cruising party, I thought. Harry was leaving us at Mawlaik and there had been an unspoken goodbye between us all day, a kindness in his eyes and in his voice that I had forgotten. Earlier, he had been entertaining the boys with party tricks and he was now getting them excited about the journey ahead. An air of anticipation and good humour swept through the boat.

We were hanging over the side, looking at the shore, when I caught sight of a conspicuous figure.

'Who's that, Vera?'

He was stalking up and down the cobbled quay as we arrived at Mawlaik as if he hadn't seen our boat with its excited load – a short, bald man with a beard. As the mooring ropes were secured and the gangplank held firmly, he strode aboard with remarkable agility, his thick-set body swaying a bit with the motion of the plank. He answered the expectant greeting from the saloon with the curtest of nods.

'All of you must disembark here in Mawlaik and camp until you get further instructions.'

There was some attempt at protest, which was met by a peremptory response: 'These are the orders!' He swept us all with a cursory look, then announced, 'Let me make it clear that you will not be permitted to make any unrestricted movements from here.' He then turned around smartly and walked away.

No one spoke. Then Ben's shrill voice suddenly shattered the silence: 'Is he the King?'

Everyone started talking at once and rushed to gather their bags together and say goodbyes. Vera ushered the two boys off the boat, and she was still both amused and embarrassed by Ben's contribution when I joined her. But I was worried.

We stood around on the shore, uncertain. Harry joined us after supervising Appaswamy and some local men to bring our luggage off the boat.

'Listen, Laura,' he said, pulling me round by the arm, 'you can't let that man stop you going on to Sittaung. You and Vera are going to have to leave with the boys without his permission, if you're going to get away at all. Otherwise you could all end up being stuck here and we don't know how long for. They did warn us that they were going to close the Tamu road to evacuees. It looks as if they're meaning to keep everyone here.'

I felt my breath shorten. So far everything had gone to plan, but now they could keep us in the camp for days – days we couldn't afford to lose. Harry nudged my arm and motioned to some small, bedraggled launches which were tied to palm trees and stakes in the muddy bank.

'Right,' he said, 'that's your answer over there. Stay here.'

He went swiftly over to a group of village men who were puffing on green cigars, and I could see that there was quite an extended negotiation. When he came back, he had secured what seemed to be the smallest and least appealing vessel of them all, a ferry boat scheduled to leave for Sittaung the next day. Harry would sleep overnight in the company bungalow, to make an early start in the morning. The rest of us were waved aboard the ferry for the night by the *serang*, who leaned indifferently against the side, his foot on the rail and a lighted *beedi* in his hand.

It suddenly all felt too hurried. As we were being bustled onto the boat, Vera was complaining into my ear and I had to beg her to go ahead, releasing Tommy's grip from my sleeve and gently getting him to hold on to the side of his mother's slacks. I could see Harry by the light from the boat and the fires burning on the shore, just standing there with his bag, his hat set to one side, and I half ran back to him.

He took both my hands in his and kissed them, then tipped my head up and said, 'Goodbye, old girl. I know you'll take care of yourself.'

Then we hugged and I pressed my hands against his back and felt the heat of his chest against my face.

'Goodbye, Harry,' I said. 'Kiss the dog for me.'

He swung his bag over his shoulder, looked at me for a moment with a flicker of a smile, then turned and moved off quickly.

8

LAURA

February 1942

Later in the evening, we sat on the cramped deck of the ferry in broken chairs. There was a space between us where Harry had been.

I was tired and longed for a bed with clean sheets. We started to feel uneasy as it became clear that we were the only ones flaunting official orders to stay put. The river no longer offered any reassurance, in contrast to the comforting glow from kerosene lamps on shore. We could hear snatches of music coming from the European club, blown across by a light breeze. Mawlaik seemed quite cheery and it was tempting to believe that we had no real reason to go on. Then, when quiet descended, we could hear the noise of the cicadas vibrating relentlessly in a nearby thicket and, sweet in the night air, the wistful sounds of a bamboo flute.

The next morning I woke up to the familiar throb of an engine, but there was little else that was similar to our previous boat. In the morning light I could see the dirt and general untidiness all around us. The boys ran around chasing cockroaches and after a while Vera gave up trying to stop them.

The river had become narrower and the water shallow. By mid-morning the heat was stifling and Vera and I chatted in desultory fits and starts. She was scornful of any notion that the Japanese could succeed in pushing us out of Burma and hadn't really wanted to leave Mandalay. But now, she said, she was glad to be going and hoped, frankly, that she could persuade Peter to leave Burma for good when it was all over. She missed the autumn in Scotland, she said, when the colours were miraculous – ochres, gold and copper – just before the leaves relinquished their tenuous hold. I listened, smiling, but I thought: I was born here. These are the people I know. This heat. These contours.

'Well, you may have to wait quite a while for autumn,' I said.

*

At midday, the *serang* came in with the ship's logbook.

'Sign,' he said, putting a well-thumbed register on the table.

'When do we get to Sittaung?' I couldn't resist asking. The *serang* collected the register and moved towards the door.

'Two o'clock.'

Two more hours and then we'd be at the start of our trek! The boat was churning up cascades of water, and suddenly a siege of snow white herons flew alongside.

We manoeuvred our way across the jetty at Sittaung – a single palm trunk laid across the mud. As we walked up the slope of the shore, Vera and I started talking about how we were going to arrange for porters for the two *dhoolies*, which would carry the boys, and for all our luggage. Harry and I had discussed it endlessly in the days before we left Rangoon. We would have to cover about thirteen miles from Sittaung to Pyambu, our first overnight stop.

'We don't really know how the trek plan is going to work out, do we,' I said to Vera, 'but we should be able to complete the whole distance easily enough on our first day as long as the boys don't have to walk. Then we can make that our first stop.'

'How long will it take, Mummy?' Tommy was pulling at Vera's arm.

'Well, if we start at about five o'clock in the morning, we ought to be in by about two or three in the afternoon, taking it quite easy. It's about three or four times round the Kokine Lakes, darling.'

Vera made it sound like an afternoon stroll. Tamu, on the border with India, was less than forty miles away, but I knew that the track would take us through thick jungle, with some stiff hill climbing. From what we understood, there would be food available in the camps. Both Vera and I had brought supplies with us – tinned beef, biscuits and marmite, as well as tea, sugar and powdered milk – and we had already dug into them on the country boat from Kalewa. We had eaten fresh fruit and vegetables on the steamer, the cook bargaining heavily along the way with the villagers, who were selling at exorbitant prices. Our own fresh supplies had long been exhausted in the days since leaving Rangoon and Mandalay. We agreed that the best thing would be to look for any fresh food before setting out and pool all our emergency rations, resorting to them only when we could see how the trek was going.

We stayed that night in a bungalow belonging to the Irrawaddy Flotilla Company, avoiding the transit camp that had been set up by the Bombay Burmah Trading Corporation. It was probably going to be our last experience of relative comfort, but I couldn't enjoy it, feeling anxious about what lay ahead. Vera had flung down a challenge in her smart outfit and was keeping up a studied air of normality. In a way I was grateful to her for that, although I wondered how long it would last.

In the evening, after we'd eaten, we walked down by the river with an elderly Indian gentleman who was to join our group on the trek. He was a cloth merchant whose shop had been burnt down by *dacoits* and was hoping, he told us, to join his wife and children in Karachi. He wanted to try out his *dhoolie* for the following day. Chin porters had strapped cross-bamboo seats across two long bamboo poles. When they had finished fixing sturdy bent twigs for the back and arm rests, he climbed in and the four Chins lifted it up. The men were of different heights and the bamboo was young and pliable. The precarious-looking contraption swayed and the length of creeper used for tying the seats split.

'Never mind, never mind. Try it out,' the man said nervously, spreading his legs out to keep his balance.

The porters started out in an uneven trot and the litter began to swing crazily. They shifted the load from one shoulder to another, heaving the bamboo shafts over their heads as the man clung desperately to the seat. Tommy and Ben started falling about on the ground, giggling. We said our farewells for the night, then Vera and I ushered the boys away, hoping that the canvas *dhoolies* that she had packed for them would be more reliable.

*

The next morning the dawn was clear and blue, with faint splashes of colour streaking the sky. When I pointed it out to the boys, Tommy said, 'Yummy, just like a Russian cake.'

Plumes of grey smoke rose thinly into the air from the little campfires. Appaswamy had taken charge and cooked our breakfast early. He was proving a boon. He was a small man, energetic, with a cheerful manner. Away from his usual household role, he seemed more relaxed and had quickly made friends with the boys.

I drank my hot tea slowly, walking to and fro and thinking about the days ahead, then rolled up our bedding and the mosquito nets. Vera was moving around putting the boys' things together. Their *dhoolies* looked serviceable enough as we adjusted the hang on the poles. I smiled as I remembered the elderly Indian the night before.

The boys rushed boisterously over to them, falling over each other in a race to get there first and then clambering in somewhat cautiously. Vera and I were feeling a new surge of enthusiasm. When we'd arrived in Sittaung the night before, we'd managed to secure ten Chin porters and a sturdy pony to carry the children, all of the luggage, bedrolls, and our supplies. Eight of the porters now lifted the *dhoolies* between them, with the two boys, and some bedding and other bundles stuffed alongside them, at first tentatively and then making a show that they made nothing of the weight. Ben's *dhoolie* was hoisted up so high that it took him by surprise and he clutched the sides frantically, tipping it so far that he fell out, descending gracefully into a pile of soft baggage. It was as good a way to start the trek as any, with us all laughing and releasing our nerves – even the porters. I felt really glad to have the boys there. They were a distraction from the mess we were leaving and my own anxieties for the future. When we reached India we would have to face a new reality and all it brought with it.

We were starting out in a small group that included some Indian evacuees, although most of the Indians, as Vera said pointedly, were supposed to be taking the longer track from

Kalewa through the Kabaw Valley. As well as the elderly gentleman of the night before, there was also a young woman, who had little more than a couple of bundles with her, which she kept strapped to her back. She was wearing what had been a smart deep-blue sari with a finely-woven border, but the hem was already dirty and torn in several places. She carried a round-eyed baby in her arms. He looked healthy and immaculate in his tiny pith helmet and little patent leather shoes.

So we set off, a curious procession, with the Chin porters striking out on the track ahead, those carrying the boys immediately in front of us. As we started, Vera danced behind, waving her hands in the air, singing in her clear voice, '*My old man said follow the van.*' I could see small hands waving as the boys shrieked with laughter and then I joined in, Tommy and Ben shouting out, '*Don't dilly dally,*' at the top of their voices. We then worked our way through half a dozen mountain walking and marching songs; at some point I led us off into '*It's a long way to Tipperary*' in a rather breathless voice, while Tommy, who by then had decided to walk, waved his arms around, conducting.

*

The path on that first day was little more than a Forestry Department track. We were soon walking relentlessly uphill. The way was strewn with evidence of those who had climbed before us and who had discarded possessions and coats on the roadside, probably as they became aware of the rigours of the upward climb. This seemed unwise, I said to Vera, as it would be cold in the high mountain ranges after Tamu. Our companions added to our anxiety. The cloth merchant frequently trailed behind us, while the young woman with the baby looked frail. She was wearing thin leather sandals and she slipped and stumbled on the uphill track. The boys were running around, and Vera suggested putting the baby in a *dhoolie*.

'Please, let the baby share with Ben,' Vera said.

The woman looked up and hesitated.

Vera smiled and said, 'It's all right, our boys are in perfectly good health. We came straight from Mandalay by boat and we have all been inoculated. There's absolutely nothing wrong with them. Please don't be worried that the little one will get any fevers from the boys.'

The woman looked embarrassed.

'I think I am seeming rude,' she said. 'But I am a doctor's wife, you know. I worry about all this sickness. There is so much cholera in the camps and the babies cannot tolerate it. Even so many are dying. This is our only child yet.'

'Of course, we understand. Dump him in. It will be easier for you . . . please.'

As the porters settled the *dhoolies* again, I asked our new companion where the doctor was.

'He is somewhere between Mawlaik and Sittaung. He is too busy to leave just now,' she said quietly.

'And are you going straight through?'

'Yes, but I am planning to spend a day or two at each camp because of the baby, if it is possible.'

*

As we approached the end of our first day's trek, our early morning enthusiasm had long since evaporated. We had taken several breaks, but by the end of the morning our feet were already blistered and painful. We were alarmed, as it was still only the first day. It had been uphill all the way and we knew it could only get worse.

'I'm scared to look at mine,' Vera said. 'I feel that if I stop now, I shall never start again . . . Oh, no!'

She broke off and hobbled after the porters, who were scrambling up the side of the hill with the *dhoolies*, Tommy and Ben hanging on to the sides, straining to keep a balance. I had heard the sound of brass bells earlier and it had come nearer, and then three elephants lumbered past us, their mahouts ridiculing the Chins who, it seemed, were getting well out of the way.

Once the elephants had passed, I clambered up the hill after the men, gesturing them to come back.

The head porter was vocal in his protests. 'Elephants not good, memsahib. Always if we see elephant, we will run or elephant will charge. My father told me, don't go in elephant track.'

Once they had come tentatively back to the path, Vera set the boys to rights and I sat hunched up on some stones with the doctor's wife, looking back down at the steepness of our climb. I could hear a few more exclamations of 'elephants not good', and when Vera joined me again she pulled a face and said, 'Heavens, that was a bit of a close thing. Let's hope we don't meet too many elephants on our travels.'

As we came round a bend, we finally caught a glimpse of the camp at Pyambu, at the top of another hill. The porters were already at the start of the track, which was wending upwards. Vera and I stopped for a minute, looking around us, trying to get a good sense of the distance we had already covered.

'I suppose it will feel better tomorrow,' I said, 'when we get used to the walking.'

I felt drained and, once we set off again, kept my eyes fixed on the track. The singing earlier in the day had reminded me of evenings in the Hut at Kokine. Mouse or Robert, or one of the girls, would play the piano, and Bobby would sometimes bring out his clarinet.

'There's a long, long trail a-winding
To the land of my dreams . . .'

The melancholy tune repeated itself in my brain. I looked across at Vera as the mat huts of the evacuation camp came properly into view on the next hillside.

'Vera!' I shouted. 'Thank goodness! That's our first day's trek over.'

*

The next day we set out early. It was one of those warm, lazy mornings. The sun formed flickering patterns of gold on the

103

dry earth and we could hear the leaves fluttering in what seemed to be perpetual movement. Ben lay spreadeagled in the brown canvas *dhoolie*, spectacles glinting in the sun, his rather fat little sunburnt legs balanced against the sides. He pushed his sun hat up and squashed it behind his head.

'Listen, Tommy. If all those leaves were soldiers,' he said, 'if all of the leaves on all those trees were soldiers, I bet we could've beaten the Japanese – easy as anything.'

Tommy sounded serious. 'No, I don't think we could've, but if all the leaves were aeroplanes, you know, air support, they would all come swooping down.'

There was a loud groan from one of the porters. Tommy had jerked almost to a sitting position and was swinging his arms around. Another of the men motioned for the boys to sit still.

'Do you think we're too heavy?' Ben asked.

'We must weigh at least a ton or two, or a hundredweight. Mummy,' Tommy called, 'how much do I weigh?'

'Too much, darling. Just keep still.' Vera and I caught up with the boys.

'Do you like riding like this, Tommy?' Ben said. 'We're having fun, aren't we?'

'Don't be silly, Ben,' Tommy said. 'We would rather be at home, wouldn't we, Mummy?'

Vera interrupted them suddenly. 'Come on boys, hop down for a while. It's time you ran around for a bit.'

The porters must have thought her sharp tones were directed at them, because they broke into a trot. Both Vera and I rushed after them, Vera screaming, 'Stop! Put the *dhoolies* down. *Jaldi! Jaldi!*' Spurred on, the porters continued at quite a pace. Vera was shouting at the men in unintelligible Hindustani. The boys sat up again with a jerk and suddenly the porters came to an abrupt halt, the *dhoolies* swaying dangerously. Tommy leant over the side of his to see how close they were to the edge and it tilted perilously over a sheer drop. He let out a yelp and Vera, almost hysterical, grabbed the edge of the canvas. Then Ben burst into noisy crying and struggled to get out, setting his own *dhoolie* swaying wildly.

'Down,' I shouted. 'Put them down!' Then, magically, the boys were lowered to the ground.

'We ought to have parachutes, really,' Tommy said in a matter-of-fact tone as he scrambled out.

'If we'd fallen out,' Ben continued his brother's train of thought, pausing to sniff loudly and pushing his spectacles back on his nose, 'we would've clung to that tree over there.' Bending over, Ben pointed to a large flowering tree, the top of which was level with the track.

'Come away from the edge!' Vera's voice was a shriek, making me jump.

*

In the morning we called out an occasional cheery encouragement to others on the track or from time to time shared some of our precious water. I explained to Tommy that we were lucky because we'd come by train and boat, and just had the hills to walk through. Some of the children here, I said, have walked with their mothers for miles and miles along the road as well, and couldn't get on a boat like us.

'That's stupid!' Ben said.

'You're stupid yourself!' Tommy started poking Ben with a small stick and we had to separate them.

It was fiercely hot by midday and the meagre water ration from the camp was giving out. Vera and I both gave most of our water to the boys; by the afternoon my head was swimming. We had walked through jungle and reached the top of a high ridge from where we could look down on the valley below and the hills beyond.

Ahead of us there was a ragged army of refugees moving across the ribbon track in untidy groups. At times it was almost an exhilarating experience, to be walking along with so many others; it was as though something else was taking control, as if individual tragedies were submerged in the sheer size of the thing. We came across bamboo *dhoolies*, too flimsily and insecurely constructed, which had already been discarded, and their broken frames lay scattered around. Most of our fellow evacuees on the track had porters or servants with them to help with their luggage and were travelling in organised groups. But some seemed to have been left behind and were struggling on their own; there were some older people who were evidently finding the climb difficult. From time to time we passed people who had started out before us that day, who were sleeping at the side of the path or sitting, exhausted.

As we walked round a bend, we saw a man walking alone, stiffly and slowly. When we came up to him, it was clear that he was blind. His bamboo staff was roughly painted, the white paint scarce in some parts and thickly and heavily painted in others. His stick tapped dangerously close to the edge of the path.

'Are you walking by yourself?' I asked, as I caught up with him.

'Yes, memsahib. I am too slow for the others, you see.'

'Can't he tag along with us?' whispered Vera. I looked at the porters. 'Why don't we fix him second last,' Vera suggested, 'and the last one can keep an eye on him.'

I asked one of the porters to hold on to the end of the stick and lead the man up the path. 'We will all go together,' I said to him.

As we started out again, Vera said, 'Shouldn't he have been on the other route? He could probably have been taken by bullock cart.'

'And paid a small fortune for the privilege,' I replied. 'If he had a small fortune.'

Some minutes later the doctor's wife turned towards us, stumbling for a moment against a boulder.

'People say that the route from Mawlaik is very difficult, you know. Very hilly, very bad, and the people are getting ill. They are pushing the Indians that way only.'

'What about the track from Kalewa?' Vera said. 'People were leaving our boat at Kalewa. It seems that there was an organised route.'

'We heard that officials are keeping evacuees in the camps for a long time. But no one wants to stay there because they are scared. And they don't have food and don't want to get ill. Look what happened at Prome when the government closed the Arakan road. So many people stuck in the camps at Prome, isn't it? So much sickness. We heard that people were dying there. Very terrible, you know. My husband was saying that there was no planning.'

'Well,' I said, 'this way we'll get to Tamu in a few days. We had friends that came this way in January and they arrived safely, so we don't worry.' I smiled at her.

Vera looked uncomfortable. Oh my dear, I thought, you can't accept the British being criticised by an Indian.

We all walked on without talking, and then Vera suddenly called out, 'Look at the china grass over there. Isn't it lovely?' There were patches of the dark green plant at the side of the road, patterned by sunflecks, four to five feet high, a thick gently-swaying carpet of it. 'Just think,' she said, 'I have it in pots at home and here there's just masses of it growing wild.'

'It is lovely, isn't it?' I said, and the moment passed.

*

The following day we were out on the road by six-thirty. The camp had a nurse and we left our blind companion in her hands, hoping that he could link up with another group. We'd slept the night in a long bamboo matting shed, rolling out our bedding onto uncomfortable bamboo cots. The boys had an early meal before falling asleep in our arms. Soon after, Vera and I had collapsed exhausted onto our own cots, but I had a fretful night.

The food provided had been sparse and unappetising; we ate some rice and dal with the last of our fresh provisions from Sittaung. The conditions in and around the camp were filthy. We gathered that numbers on the track had been increasing throughout February; now the sanitation was breaking down and people were relieving themselves where they could. This is going to get worse, I thought. I was glad to move on, although my legs felt tired and weak from the previous day's uphill climb. The baby had developed dysentery and we had to leave the doctor's wife behind us so that he could be treated, saying our goodbyes as cheerfully as we could.

We had come down steeply into the valley to reach the camp the previous day, the porters and the little pony making a precarious descent with the luggage and the *dhoolies*. The final part of the day's march had taken its toll on our legs and feet, leaving us with cramped and pulled muscles and tendons. As we headed out towards Tamu our feet didn't get any better despite being well padded with the plasters we had brought with us – an essential part of our first-aid supplies. The stones were sharp, even through our walking shoes, and our blisters had become raw.

Vera sat down suddenly. 'Just a minute. It's because of these beastly things.'

She took off her brogues. The leather was rubbing and her feet were swollen, with the nails of her inflamed toes blue and bleeding, while a blister oozed out of one heel where the plasters had been rubbed away. She pulled off her petticoat and tore it into strips, and then started bandaging her feet with swathes of the material.

'Civilisation recedes,' I laughed.

Vera pulled a face. 'I'm afraid I shall have to do without shoes for today and without a petticoat till I get to India; and I know I should wear slacks again tomorrow anyway. I'm getting bitten to death.' She picked her way lightly and carefully along the track. We were going so slowly that a few groups of trekkers passed us.

Our elderly companion went past in his *dhoolie*, then stopped and called out. He stepped unsteadily out of the cane seat.

'Memsahib, please will you ease your feet in this?' He must have been looking at the way Vera was edging carefully along the softer edges of the track.

Vera looked embarrassed. 'No, thank you very much,' she replied. 'It's only for a little way and my feet will soon be all right.'

'Your feet are not used to stones, isn't it? How can you now walk?'

'Well, these days there are stranger things happening,' I said, trying to be cheerful.

I started to shuffle around, feeling impatient. We needed to keep moving and the boys' *dhoolies* were no longer within view.

I looked anxiously along the track ahead. The old man must have seen my look because he turned to Vera again, staring at her bandaged feet. The white silk had taken on the colour of the road, and the material was already worn and frayed. There were ugly, inflamed bites around her ankles.

'Now, memsahib, please.'

'No, thank you. You are very kind,' Vera said.

Our companion reluctantly got back into his *dhoolie* and fifteen minutes later we had caught up with the boys, who were anxious to get down and walk.

The boys were in high spirits and pleaded with us to sing.

'*Boots, boots, boots, boots,*' Tommy started us off and we all joined in.

> '*Movin' up and down again,*
> *Try, try, try, try . . .*'

'Oh no!' Vera started giggling, 'Don't make me think about my feet!' But she was shouted down.

'*There's NO DISCHARGE IN THE WAR.*'

*

Early in the afternoon, at the end of the third day of our trek, we came along a quiet jungle track into Tamu and soon became absorbed into a much larger crowd of evacuees pouring in from the south along the Kalewa-Tamu road. What had been an obscure little village just one and a half miles from the Indian border had grown overnight. We passed the Circuit House on the right, the Court House on the left, both swarming with people. After we'd joined the queues to register at the evacuation office, I left Vera with the boys outside while I pushed through the crowds in the post office to send off a telegram. I sent one to Harry and also another three: to Lion in Pegu, to Robert, and to my aunt Louisa at the Calcutta address they'd forwarded to Rangoon.

Vera had been worrying about her husband, and I got off a telegram to him for her. When I joined her forty minutes or so later, she was telling the boys brightly that we should be proud of all the men because they were fighting off the enemy, and that the British had the best army, so the Japs would soon all be scuttling off home. I told her I'd sent the telegrams and she closed her eyes and made a sort of prayer: 'Peter, please be all right.'

The camp was out of town and I felt incredibly weary as we trudged slowly towards it. As we got nearer, we could hear a noise rising up into the still evening, like the deep buzz of an angry hive.

'Look, Auntie Laura,' shouted Tommy, pulling at my arm. 'People! There are hundreds of them.'

'Thousands,' declared Ben.

'One . . . two . . . three millions.'

'Billions!'

'Trillions!' Tommy was triumphant.

'Oh, stop it you two!' I shouted at them. They were becoming impossible and I suddenly found our arrival immensely depressing. This didn't feel like safety. Every inch of ground was heaving with people, and the air was stifling and foul-smelling. Vera grabbed the two boys.

'Keep still and stay with me or you'll get lost.'

I was making my way through the crowd when I caught sight of a woman who smiled at me and gave me a quick wave. As she moved towards me, I still couldn't place her although I knew her face. She was in her mid-twenties, Anglo-Burmese, with soft eyes, a wide, sweet mouth and a black mole on her upper lip.

'Mrs Ferguson, how are you? I saw you coming in.'

I stared at her, feeling the last dregs of energy suddenly drain from me.

'I'm stupid! You probably don't remember me. I was wearing my nurse's uniform then. I'm Julia Steele.'

I remembered her. It was three years before. She had been there for my dark time. I remembered her voice. Warm. Solicitous. I made an effort to smile.

'I'm so sorry. It took me a moment, but of course . . .'

There was a flash of recognition between us. Then she gave me a careful smile. 'How are you? And your wonderful husband? I suppose the company won't let him go.'

'He's fine, thank you,' I said. Then, searching for something to say, I mumbled, 'Please excuse us. We must look horrendous.' My trousers were filthy and seemed to have lost all shape. My shirt felt slightly damp, and I tugged it away from my skin, where it clung uncomfortably.

'Don't worry,' Julia said, 'you can freshen up here. I'm with some friends. I was watching you come in and you all looked so tired.' She reached forward to me and shouted above the noise, 'Come and join us. We've got a cup of tea going over there – away from all the people.'

Vera had pushed through the mass of refugees with the boys, and I introduced her. Julia smiled at Tommy and Ben.

The thought of tea was wonderful and when I turned to Vera, she looked exhausted and beaten. I quickly grabbed her arm and exclaimed to Julia, 'That would be marvellous. Otherwise it will take us hours to sort ourselves out and we might all just pass away before we get anything.'

*

As she led us through the tightly-pressed mass of people, Julia told us a little about the others who were trekking with her. She and her friends had arrived on the track from Mawlaik. Our conversation was snatched as we pushed through. It seemed they had come from the transit camp at Hlezeik, the last one before coming in to Tamu.

'We arrived here yesterday,' she said, 'but they're not letting us go on yet. We've got to get a permit to leave Burma.'

'Why are you being held? Is no one going?'

'They're trying to control the numbers on the road – at least that's what's being said. We're hoping it won't be more than a couple of days. Anyway,' she said, 'you might be glad for a rest before you go on. Our camp's not too bad, and it's away from all this crowd.'

The idea of a few days' rest sounded good; I felt relieved not to have to think of moving off again the next morning. The children had become fractious; Vera had been making a huge effort to encourage the boys to keep going but she was becoming anxious. As we moved off again, we both kept a firm hold of each boy by the hand.

Julia led us though the tightly-packed crowd. The one or two Europeans I could see looked as if they might be officials. The evacuees were overwhelmingly Indians of all classes and descriptions, family groups, crying children and servants. We pushed our way past a man with thick, oiled moustaches, his white muslin trousers soiled and dusty from the road and incongruous over thick brown shoes, which were flapping open as he walked. He held luggage in one hand and had a dog firmly gripped under his other arm. His wife was carrying a baby, while two shaven-headed children half-trotted behind them, holding on to the hems and edges of their clothing.

'A lot of these people came along the Kalewa route,' Julia said. 'They've probably been away from their homes for weeks.'

I thought about the deck travellers on the steamer who had disembarked at Kalewa; they would still be on the road somewhere. It seemed that now, whatever route we had arrived on, we were all going to join up on the track across the border into India and over the Naga Hills.

After much pushing and shoving, we came up to a group gathered around kerosene burners and small fires. Julia waved, calling out to a young woman sitting on a small camp stool. I badly needed something to eat and drink, and the thought of hot tea was heavenly. I drove away memories.

The woman jumped up and held her hand out in welcome, introducing herself as Gracie Shaw. She was tall and striking looking, with full, upturned lips and almost perfect eyebrows, black wings which tapered into the thinnest of lines. She was about the same age as Julia, with thick hair, cut into a heavy, somewhat old-fashioned fringe, and a sprinkling of freckles on her nose. She looked at least five months pregnant. I froze for a moment as she gripped my hand.

'And this is Lucy.' Julia's voice was bright and she turned me gently towards a short young woman, not long out of her teens, with a dull brown complexion, well-built, with heavy hips and legs. She had an astonishing square aspect to her jaw and high cheek bones. I found her gaze somewhat disturbing, but then she smiled almost brilliantly at us and looked cheerfully down at Tommy, who was exhausted and was leaning against me. Ben was still clutching Vera's hand and was swinging around on one leg; Lucy moved towards him and tousled his hair.

I tried to absorb the surprise of meeting Julia and to ignore a familiar sickness in the pit of my stomach that it had caused. In many ways I felt a huge relief as we sat down to our picnic. The girls had spread a towel on the ground; there were tins of tea, milk and sugar, and then biscuits and jam. An aluminium kettle was boiling on a fire built of dried twigs, and the hissing steam was somehow comforting. Once we sat down, Ben fell asleep with his thumb in his mouth, his eyes rolling upwards. We had got through. It would be okay.

'Do you know, they have been warning us that the second half of the trek is worse than the first.' Lucy must have been reading my mind. She continued, 'It's about fifty miles to Palel, where the bus goes from. But don't get too encouraged. We're only at about six hundred feet above sea level here, and we're going to have to go up to almost six thousand feet. It's real mountain walking. Can you imagine?'

'We've been trying not to think about it,' Vera replied, with an edge to her voice. 'I just don't know how we're going to make it with the boys and the luggage.'

'Maybe it won't seem so bad after you've had some tea and a good rest. Can you dump some of your luggage? That's what a lot of people are deciding to do. And you'd better check out whether the boys will be able to stay in the *dhoolies*. It's supposed to be a good stiff climb in places.'

Lucy gently disentangled Ben from Vera to leave her free to eat. She was sitting cross-legged on the ground and Ben snuggled comfortably into her lap, his head resting against her chest.

She seemed sensible, I thought, and was probably right about the luggage, but I couldn't think about that for now. We had yet to make arrangements for sleeping, and I was feeling daunted by the thought of fighting through the crowd again to sort it out. Julia was leaning forward and talking to the woman introduced as Gracie, who glanced at us once or twice. Then Julia turned to Vera.

'We've got little cabins in the sleeping shelter, and the one next to ours might still have some space – the people left today. So you should get up there quite quickly, don't you think? You could peg your claim by putting stuff in it straightaway.'

Vera and I looked at each other in relief and then Vera burst into tears, her hands over her face and her shoulders shaking. I had seen it coming but I felt worried about her and kept my arm around Tommy.

Julia leant forward and touched Vera on the knee. 'We can also make room on the bunk in our cabin. One of you could have the space if you need it.'

'It's just the boys,' Vera said. 'I feel so anxious about them.'

'We're all quite healthy, so please don't worry.' Julia's voice was reassuring. She turned towards me. 'If you want to go up to our little camp, it's just beyond that crowd – about half way between the town and the Lockchau River. It's an ideal site, really. It won't take me a minute to tell the men how to get there as I've just about got the geography of this place worked out now – you have to go up past the main camp, which is for Indians. There's hot water up there and I bet you are all dying for a wash. And perhaps we could go up to the river later on. Would that be okay?'

It sounded okay to me. It sounded wonderful. After we had tea, we sent one of the porters back to look out for the others as they carried the luggage in.

With our new friends taking charge, I was pleased to no longer have to look out for the boys and lay back on the ground, letting my mind wander.

*

Julia entered my side ward for the first time the day after they took the baby away from me. She had brought in flowers from Harry, and they carried with them a sweet smell that I could never again bear to be near. She just came to the side of my bed, with a swish of her starched uniform, and took my hand. She would be there, she said, not far away, whenever I needed her. And she checked my drips and plumped the pillows. Eloise, my baby, had lived for only ten minutes and from then on my life no longer made sense.

For months before the birth my days had been charged with heightened emotions, and I woke every morning as if it were a celebration. For the first time I was Aunt Louisa's favourite. My cousins sewed baby clothes and fussed around me endlessly. Harry became loving and attentive. He would come home from the club early and drank less. We would often just sit comfortably together in the evening listening to music, reading or playing cards. When I was about four months gone there was a moment when I looked up from my book after dinner. Harry had put the paper down; he was simply sucking on his pipe and staring at me. Then he came over and knelt down in front of me with his face against my belly and said, 'Well, old girl, it's just about you and the baby now!'

I drifted into sleep.

*

I woke up to a commotion around us. Appaswamy and the porters had arrived with the bags, and I heard Ben's distressed voice above it all. He needed to go to the toilet urgently. Lucy said that she would take him, explaining that the trenches were filthy and they had their own private place. Vera went with them and I got Tommy involved in checking off our luggage with Appaswamy while I talked to the porters.

A little later we worked our way steadily through the dense crowd. I had never seen so many women together before. It felt comfortable in a way I couldn't quite understand, a sort of enveloping mass strength, a sense of common purpose. My spirits lifted a little. Looking around, the few men were instantly noticeable.

Julia pointed out a Sikh who was passing our group. 'Be careful,' she said, 'he's one of the doctors – very good, very concerned – so watch out for any medicines you have with you or he will grab them for his patients.'

Our camp was about a mile uphill from the main one – a long hut divided into cabins, with a separate eating area. We were relieved to find empty cots in the cabin next to the women. I worked together with Vera to unpack a few things and, after the boys were settled in for the night, she said that she needed to sleep before she collapsed and was happy to stay with them while I walked out of the camp with the others. 'Don't fall off a cliff,' she said, in a weak attempt at a joke.

Julia took us along the jungle path above the camp leading to the Lockchau. Over the last days the streams had been foul, filled with effluence, and we had kept away from them. Here, we were told, the river was running clear. There was water for washing in the camp, so we felt happy to just paddle. The river was quite wide, but we were able to get down to a small shore. I had changed out of my trousers into a dress, and I now pulled up the hem and walked gingerly into the icy water on my broken bare feet until it nearly reached my knees. The mountains were hidden by a screen of jungle foliage and it was almost a relief to be free of the heights and gorges, and the endless panoramas. It was so peaceful that we were reluctant to go back to the camp, and instead I wandered with the women up the hill which marked the boundary between Burma and India.

9

BOBBY

February 1942

In the days before the fiasco of 22 February, when the Sittang bridge was blown with our chaps on the wrong side of the river, Pegu was in a state of confusion, with the army commandeering anything on four wheels. Somehow or other, Lion managed to get hold of an American lease-lend jeep from one of the transport pounds, got his papers and moved out of Pegu, leaving me in his house. After Moulmein was abandoned, it was crucial to hold Kyaikhto to prevent the Japanese advance towards Rangoon and northwards into Central Burma, and our 16th and 48th Brigades were ordered to retreat back up to Kyaikhto. My orders were to go down there from Pegu on what was a jungle track of sorts, to pick up the post and telecommunications personnel.

When I got there on the evening of the 20th, our men were struggling in, exhausted, many of them wounded from the constant air attacks. What was happening was a race between our troops and the Japanese for the Sittang bridge, and when we headed back to Sittang that night along the narrow jungle path, the personnel packed into the jeep, the Japanese had already intercepted our orders for withdrawal and were steadily encircling our troops.

Ismail drove us steadily, his nerves steel, while I kept my eyes fixed on the darkness of the jungle. When the dense foliage cleared in patches, the moon threw down pools of light on the dried-up forest floor. I had seven in the back, two of the women pressed between the seats, and they were as silent as the dead. Even the usual jungle noises seemed to have faded out and all we could hear was the stuttering of gunfire. Some five miles from the bridge, we ran into such heavy fire that I ordered Ismail to stop. We leapt down beside the jeep, but held our own fire. I couldn't see anything, and the shots seemed to gain an independent presence of their own. After ten minutes or so, the gunfire moved away from us, and I started using some of the breath which had been locked into my chest. I decided it was time to be on the move again.

It was a relief when we got to the other side of the Sittang bridge, the road by then little more than a cart track running along the side of the railway, marked in the darkness by the telegraph poles of the line which linked Rangoon with southern Burma. This was rice-growing country, and I drove along an exposed sort of road, most of the way raised high on an embankment above the paddy fields. But it felt like the route to heaven after our run through the jungle, and we all shifted in our seats more easily.

The following day I took the personnel up to the railway station at Nyaunglebin, some twenty miles north, towards Taungoo. The road was packed right up to the station with evacuees from Pegu. The notice for civil evacuation from Rangoon had been given the previous day, with orders for people to leave within forty-eight hours. The result was that refugees were streaming along the Rangoon-Pegu road and were now joining the surge from the south. Indian and Chinese workers were on foot, and there were families as well, carrying as much as they could. Handcarts, bullock carts, *gharries*, bicycles – they were all surrounding and jostling with lease-lend trucks, which were moving equipment and supplies northwards, throwing up clouds of dust. As we came into town, the procession took on a frenetic character, drivers leaning out of the trucks, gesturing and swearing at the animals and foot traffic which checked their progress. The town itself was a complete shambles. As we drove past the bazaar, we could see that it had been looted the previous night. The stall fronts were hanging open on their hinges, there was debris strewn around, and there were fires raging behind the bazaar.

I spent a couple of days going back and forth on that stretch of road. I was in Pegu when the Sittang bridge was blown in the early hours of the morning of 22 February by our sappers.

I was ordered to Rangoon later that day and drove back, the sun still high over the paddy fields, my mind full of our troops caught on the other side of the Sittang river, left to surrender or swim across as best they could under constant enemy fire. I was by no means easy in the flat countryside or as we passed through the villages scattered among the paddy fields, set hard at that time of the year. The road was almost empty – too quiet after the chaos of the last few days. I held my sten gun on my knee while Ismail drove. There was no doubt that the Patriotic Burma Forces had gained ground with the *thajee*, the headmen of the village, with the promise of independence for Burma. I was beginning to realise that you could no longer count on loyalty in the villages.

As we approached the Prome Road some twenty miles north of Rangoon, we passed the Shwe Nyaungbin, the great banyan tree, the home of powerful *nats* – the spirits – the flowers in the brick shrine withered and faded. I was stopped before Kokine and we showed our papers. As we reached the neck of the lakes, I looked back over the water, the late afternoon sun shimmering on its surface. Our promontory was over in the distance, the Hut too small to see. I hadn't been in Rangoon since the civil evacuation was ordered on 20 February. Since then there had been two days and nights of heavy bombing and a pall of black smoke hung over the city.

I was told that it had been a stampede when the 'E' notice went up. It meant that only essential workers were permitted to remain in the city and to drive vehicles, and now the last of the crowds of evacuees and animals streamed along the road, out towards the lakes, to family villages, onwards to Prome or to uncertain destinations in Central and Upper Burma.

*

As I drove into Rangoon on the Prome Road, I was entering a ghost town – a graveyard of abandoned and burnt-out vehicles and equipment discarded at the side of the road. Many of the bungalows showed evidence of looting, and some had been gutted by fire. The *dacoits* had been at work, Ismail pointed out. We drove down Strand Road and then along the Sule Pagoda Road towards the station. The pagoda itself with its narrow *stupa*, standing at the intersection of streets, was untouched. All the businesses, banks and hotels were closed and the streets were empty, apart from a number of army vehicles which intruded noisily into the silence. There was an eerie stillness. I drove past the picture houses – my old haunts – almost as if on a pilgrimage, and got out of the jeep to wander around for a few minutes outside the Odeon. The orders for evacuation were posted on the walls and then, as if in mockery, on the corner of a side street, there was an old air-raid practice notice which called on citizens to stay put and not let Rangoon burn. We had seen all the burnt-out bungalows on our way through, the smell of charred wood strong in the air adding to the overall sense of desolation and decay. So much for the famous stay-put policy!

I walked back to the jeep feeling low, when suddenly a group of pariah dogs shot out in front of me, startling in the silence of the streets. Then shots rang out from the side streets, setting off a chorus of barking.

'Looters!' Ismail said, shrugging his shoulders.

When we arrived at HQ, I was feeling exhausted and went through to the canteen after reporting in. Part of HQ personnel had already left for Maymyo, but I found Butler there, a sergeant major, an Anglo-Burman I had known back in 1939 when he had worked briefly for Philips with me.

'Lieutenant Stapleton! Don't tell me you have left that lot back there to fight the Japs on their own!'

I didn't feel like smiling, but he was an open, friendly sort and I found myself talking to him about the last few days and discussing the virtual destruction of the 17th Infantry Division at the Bilin River and the disaster at the Sittang Bridge. It seemed that the talk at headquarters now was not so much about whether Rangoon would be fully evacuated, but when, and when the Japanese would take the city. The sacrifice at Bilin seemed almost pointless.

'Well, the Japs won't find much when they get here, I can tell you that. And they'll have a nice little surprise waiting for them with all the convicts and lunatics wandering up and down.' Butler lit his cigarette.

I was aware that there was a lot of talk about the civilian population being half-scared to death by the release of the inmates from the prison and from the mental hospital.

'They say that the inmates have started some of these fires. Is that true?' I asked.

'Well, that's what they say, but there are all sorts on the streets now. The *dacoits* have come in from the villages around, you see, and they reckon that's where most of the looting is coming in. I can tell you, the police don't mess about with them.' Butler stopped for a minute. 'No one seems to know just how many of these prisoners or crazy people there are wandering around. Some people say there were about five thousand of them, but that's a lot of nonsense if you ask me.'

I shook my head, thinking about what Butler was saying. He was still talking.

'They were supposed to be taken off by rail to Upper Burma. But now, they were supposed to be getting a lot of the mental patients onto the trains – whether they ever did, who knows? You should've seen the station; it's been utter chaos. Damned disgrace. The jail warders who were trying to get away to Mandalay were causing a riot trying to storm one train, and they had to be thrown off by the military police.'

I thought about the empty streets. 'What about the civilians who are supposed to be left behind for essential services? I didn't see any signs of them as I was coming through.'

'The last ditchers?' Butler replied, pushing his hair back. 'They're camped in messes near the Mogul Guard. I don't suppose they move about any more than they have to.'

*

Eva and Paul Lamont had left for Maymyo earlier in February, soon after the Japanese crossed the Salween. By then the stay-put policy had long since begun to look foolhardy and civil order seemed on the point of collapse. I was haunted by the idea of Daw Min Min alone in the house while all the rumours were flying around. I thought she must have been evacuated with all the rest, but I felt compelled to check the bungalow, to rid myself of an image of her seated at the window in an empty street. I left with Ismail later that day to go out to Kokine and was able to take a detour. As I turned into their road, I passed two bungalows that were completely gutted. One had been quite a large house, impressively set back on a wide driveway. Its charred, roofless remains now looked incongruous. The lawns were untended and dried out, although shrubs and bushes were flowering profusely.

The front windows of the house next to the Lamonts' had been smashed in and I turned into the Lamonts' driveway with some trepidation, driving the jeep up to the veranda. The cane chairs and tables were missing. I was used to seeing Lamont sitting there with his papers and books, always with a *beedi* or cigarette burning. The veranda was now bare, the hanging ferns and geraniums wilted and shrunken. Something banged and the garage door swung out slightly, its top hinge broken.

As I jumped out of the jeep, I called out, 'Ismail, you wait here while I take a look.'

I walked over and fixed the garage door in place, and went back to the house. The front door was shut, but it opened when I turned the handle, and I called Ismail over to fix the lock.

'Auntie! Auntie!'

I went into the living room, almost ready to see her sitting in one of the chairs in a corner of the room, drawing on a cigar. But the room was empty. All the furniture had gone, and also the best floor rug. The emptiness of the place got to me and I called out again. The door to Eva's room was ajar and I went in, with an uneasy sense of intimacy. The bed was stripped of linen, with the mosquito netting hanging in a crazy way across it. It was hot. There was an incessant buzzing of flies against the window. Still standing by the door, I turned the switch of the ceiling fan, but there was no current. I went over to the dressing table and rubbed my finger in the red dust beginning to accumulate on the mirror. There was a small painted silk fan on the dressing table and, next to it, a scent bottle. I picked up the scent bottle and put it in my pocket and, blowing the dust off the fan, left the bungalow with it.

The empty house had unsettled me, and I was in two minds about the trip to Kokine. Until then, I hadn't considered the possibility that the Hut might be stripped bare, or even burnt out. As we drove along the road to Kokine in the heavy mid-afternoon heat, I felt real fear, in a way that I hadn't even on the Kyaikhto forest track a few days previously. We had been living on adrenalin since the action at Sittang, but the city was so desolate I felt at my lowest point since the Christmas bombing. Rangoon seemed to be awaiting its destiny – its destruction either at our hands or those of the Japanese. There was nothing to be done to prevent it.

I looked across at Ismail. He had his hands folded gently in his lap, his eyes fixed on the road. As we approached the driveway to the Hut, I could see our twin home, looking as I'd seen it so many times coming back from work or more recently from my trips. It hadn't been burnt, but as I went into the house I could see that it had been looted. It was absurd: the locks had been broken, but the house was still surprisingly tidy. The carpets and most of the furnishings had been packed away in the *godowns* before my aunt Louisa left, and it was large items such as the huge inlaid sideboard and the piano that had been left. The piano was untouched, and I was suddenly overwhelmed by the thought – a clear image – of my father sitting at it after supper parties, and also Jo-Jo scowling over her scales and Marcie filling the house throughout one month with endless repetitions of one of Schubert's *Études*.

Ismail had been scouting around and reappeared from the back of the house, saying, 'There is nothing in kitchen, sahib. It has all been taken – pots, pans and all those things are not there. I think it's better we use our rations.'

'I'm not sure yet if we're going to stay here, Ismail.'

The boxes that had been packed and left in the storeroom were no longer there. I went down to the tennis courts. The grass was already growing quite wildly around the sides of the netting.

I ran across the front lawn, past the padauk tree, crushing unswept blossoms under my feet. The smell in the air was unbearably sweet. The boats were gone, and for one minute my eyes swept the shore of the lake, as if I might have been mistaken. I remembered one October evening, just two months before Pearl Harbour was bombed. The girls had not yet left for Calcutta. Aunt Bea and her family had come to dinner with some young officers – friends of Issie's husband. Some of us had gone on the boats out to one of the islands, taking the gramophone with us, while my father and the others had drinks. Marcie was madly teasing one of the young lieutenants, while Jo-Jo spent the whole evening whispering and giggling with her young friends, and being very superior with our cousin Thomas.

I sat down on the steps for a while with my head down, scratching the ground with a stone, then suddenly shouted out – a formless sound that emptied across the deserted lake.

That night I stayed in the Hut, surrounded by ghosts, the horizon lit by the red glow of the sky above Rangoon as the city burned. I wondered where my father was, hoping that Lion had found him in Maymyo and thinking that Aunt Bea and the Lamonts must already be there, unless Paul Lamont had persuaded Eva to leave for India already. There was talk that the authorities were blocking off the road to India through Tamu until it could be surfaced, so refugees were being held in the camps. Laura had to have got through. My mind ran on and on. As we were leaving at dawn, I slept for only two or three hours, but I woke feeling surprisingly cheerful, as always anxious to be on our way.

10

CHRISSIE

March 1986

I applied for a reader's ticket to do some research among the India Office Records in the British Museum. Towards the end of March, the week after the school term ended, I made my first trip to the imposing building near Russell Square and spent every day of the following two weeks there, excited to be part of the intense atmosphere of study in the famous round Reading Room with its beautiful domed ceiling.

The official files gave me the details I was looking for on the rush out of Rangoon at the end of December 1941 and January 1942. After the first bombing raids, tens of thousands of people set out northwards to Prome with the aim of reaching Taungup and from there to cross on foot the treacherous jungle-covered mountains which encircled the Bay of Bengal, heading for India. But then an enormous pressure of people built up at Taungup and, with no inoculation programme in place, thousands of those on the road died from cholera. But the people heading out were mainly the Indian workers who kept Rangoon on its feet – the civil servants, the clerks, the prison officials and the road sweepers, all those who provided the backbone of the workforce. It seemed that government officials rushed to Prome and blocked the Arakan road and persuaded a very large number of them to turn round and head back to Rangoon, convincing them that the Japanese would never enter Rangoon and that all was safe.

I read my father some of my notes when I next went out to Hertfordshire.

'It was madness, wasn't it, Dad? I mean the government persuaded them to come back, and in the end they had to leave again pretty quickly and things got worse and worse for them. It seems that a lot of those people died along the way later on when they got stuck in the camps in Prome or were driven north towards Mandalay. In the end many of them didn't get out at all.'

'Well, you see, Chrissie, the administration panicked. You have to remember – after the bombing, Rangoon was falling apart. There were bodies just lying in the road . . . people that had been hit by the bombs . . . and there was a terrible stench everywhere. Terrible. The drains and the sewers were overflowing. There was no one left to work in the hospitals. Everything had come to a standstill and the government was in a dreadful funk, if I can put it like that.'

Later, we came back to the same topic. My father said, 'You see the Indians were the real workers in Burma, but they were regarded as the coolie class. The British and Anglo-Burmese never mixed much with the Indians socially, although the whole set-up in Burma depended on them.'

'But that was the British raj, wasn't it – the whole white superiority thing?'

'That's true. But you see there were class divisions as well. We were used to the divisions, but it was all those things that made it easier for the authorities to leave the Indians to their own devices when it came to the evacuation of Burma.'

There was something we weren't talking about, I thought. The Family were part of it – the jostling for place in the social hierarchy. Money. Influence.

'Marcie and Jo-Jo were lucky to get out when they did,' I pointed out, 'before it all kicked off.'

'The Indians in Burma weren't all poor. Far from it; many of them were wealthy, but they had to fight to try to get on the boats and planes, whoever they were.' My father seemed caught up in reflections, thoughts that had lain undisturbed for years. 'Many of them were traders and bankers. With the tide turning, sometimes the Burmese took against them, giving vent to old resentments, I suppose, and started to burn down their shops and markets. So they felt they couldn't stay in the country.'

He took off his glasses and rubbed his eyes – serious.

Then he added, 'Of course, just as the Family did, many of them rushed to get their money to India in the weeks after the December bombing. But in the end they had to leave their homes and lives behind them, taking their chances on the road along with all the others, you know, the coolie labourers, the dock workers, the household *dhobis* and sweepers and all the rest.'

*

I wanted to read some contemporary accounts about the closing of the Rangoon mental hospital. I found several reports which gave me more details. It seemed that, by the middle of February, it became impossible to get the Indian staff at the asylum to carry on working; the shops and bazaars were closed, so there was no food to be had. There were worrying rumours about how Indians would be treated by the Japanese, and with events moving quickly, the Indian staff were given their pay and told to leave. At the same time, patients that were considered sane enough were given ten rupees and told to make their way to the railway station, while those patients who were seriously mentally disturbed were abandoned and left to their own devices.

The scandal only increased when prisoners were released from Rangoon and Insein jails onto the streets – even the most dangerous criminals who were housed in Insein jail. It caused a sensation, with reports of convicts roaming about in prison dress, joining the gangs who were coming in from the villages and looting shops and burning houses. It seemed from the files that the whole civil administration suddenly collapsed, and those in charge sought their own safety before anything else, commandeering whatever vehicles they could.

I looked across at the other library readers. We seemed almost hermetically sealed in, bent over our individual piles of papers, the slightest murmur reverberating around the domed room. From the files, it was clear that the sudden issue of Label 'E', the signal for evacuation, caused a final rush out of Rangoon, leaving the burning, empty streets patrolled by troops carrying tommy guns and rifles. It was a dystopian image. I realised that Laura had got out just in time before the final collapse. As I worked through the stacks of files they brought to my desk, I felt I could taste and smell despair in the reports of the dying city in those last weeks of February and early March 1942.

11

BOBBY

March 1942

Throughout March I drove around Central Burma as our forces gradually retired up the Prome Road, leaving the lines of communication down behind them. By the beginning of March the Japanese had four divisions in Burma and were moving up and surrounding our forces near Mandalay. I didn't find myself so much in the line of fire as I had been in the campaign around the Pegu area. On the other hand, much of Central Burma was also under constant threat of air attack from the Japanese and the entire population was increasingly nervous. The exit by boat from Burma was pretty well cut off and the route that Laura had taken from Sittaung had been blocked shortly after she'd left, the authorities being anxious to complete metalling works to provide an exit route for the troops. In fact, at one point, listening to the stories of the faltering evacuation from the camps, I became concerned that Laura was held up somewhere.

It was quite pointless worrying, but the general air of discontent and anxiety made it difficult to keep my mind purely on my job. The officials and their wives had priority for rail transport to Upper Burma and the air evacuation. It was the Indian and Anglo-Indian population that were left behind to walk out as best they could or to collect in the refugee camps. The camps became bottlenecks where the old and young children became weakened by dysentery and where, so we heard, increasing numbers were dying of cholera and typhoid.

When Ismail and I hit the road, I was glad to put behind me all the endless discussions about the failings of the government and the routes out of India. The two of us didn't chatter much when we were in the jeep. Ismail was a quiet sort of chap and I liked to keep my feelings to myself, but I got used to having him next to me. As a rule I took the wheel and we would set out early in the morning, the jungle foliage shrouded in a light mist. If I glanced at Ismail, I knew I would catch his eyes keenly alert above the non-regulation scarf, which he wrapped around his mouth and neck against the early morning chill at the end of the cold season; as temperatures rose, it served equally well to catch the dust thrown up by the jeep, which by degrees covered us with a thin red film, mixing with our sweat and leaving tracks on our cheeks and necks. The stillness of the jungle at midday was hypnotic and when the heat began to build up in March and almost burned into our nostrils, it was easily possible to be lulled by the buzzing of insects and tiny birds, the quiet broken occasionally by a strident bird call overhead. But we knew that the noise of the jeep would hide the sound of dried twigs and bracken breaking, which could as well be from a human as from an animal presence. I couldn't think of a better chap than Ismail to trust my life to.

I passed through Mandalay at the very beginning of March. It was becoming quite hot and unpleasant, and packed with refugees. It was good to see the Family – what was left of them in Burma. Lion had rented some rooms in the Burmese quarter and I went over there for the first time. It was a pretty cramped place; in fact, the whole environment around that area was foul and unhealthy, with an all-pervasive smell of night soil, which was no longer being cleaned by the sweepers. As I drove up, I wondered how the men were coping on their own.

I found my father staying in the house. He seemed pleased to see me but was looking tired and full of anxieties. He was concerned about his health and I thought his face looked grey, the eyes somewhat distant. I had bought fruit at the roadside, so we sat peeling and eating papaya as I told them about my time in Lower Burma over the previous few weeks. The terrible frustration among the civil population was evident everywhere and Lion and my father were no exception, eager to pick up every little bit of information, waiting for the news broadcasts, turning round and round the latest updates, opinions and ideas about staying or leaving the country. My feeling was that they were missing a sense of their own value in all that was going on; for the first time they had lost any belief in their power to control or influence their own lives, or were even unsure of the next step to take. Lion was able to throw all his frustration back onto the administration, which he was battling with on a daily basis, while my father was still convinced that he should be able to join in the fighting. He kept on coming back to a similar refrain. 'This age business is nonsense!' he said that evening. 'I know this country better than a lot of the young men that are here now. It doesn't make sense, Lion. You can't tell me it does!'

He did seem to gain some satisfaction from the fact that I was seeing action, but he held himself rigid while I told them of my visit to Kokine, his eyes focusing on the wall beyond as I was speaking. I found that I was trying to reassure him, or possibly myself.

'Nothing was broken, Daddy. The house is quite liveable really, although the refrigerator is mouldy, of course. Poor Fran. She was so proud of it. Oh well, that's the way it goes!' I tried to sound light-hearted.

'I don't think it was *dacoits*,' Lion chimed in. He was sitting on the edge of the table, tapping out his pipe. 'They would have taken more than you say they have, Bobby. I wouldn't be at all surprised if it were the military police. You know what the saying is: *There is never one dacoity but always two – first the dacoits and then the police.*'

'What about Bea and Lester's place?' my father asked.

I had hoped to stop the jeep on my way back from Kokine to visit the Mansion, but had run out of time. From the road the house had looked shuttered and untouched.

'I wasn't able to stop. Had to get back – you know how it is. But, from what I could see, there were no signs of any disturbance and certainly there hadn't been a fire. In fact, I think that was true for most of the property on that bit of road.'

'Good, you'd better go and tell that to your aunt Bea when you get to Maymyo, Bobby. She's taken it all very badly and she's anxious to see you.'

I headed out to the golf club and towards Mandalay Hill that evening. It was a pleasant part of the town, with its cluster of golden-tipped pagodas and the backcloth of the Shan Hills. I had trekked to the top on a visit the previous year, climbing in bare feet to the shrines and the huge golden Buddha. How things had changed in one year!

I turned in early; I was due to go to Maymyo the following day and was impatient to see Eva and her father, anxious as well to know if Daw Min Min had made her way to join them. Maymyo was a small hill station about twenty-five miles from Mandalay on the Lashio road, and the governor and his office had moved there after the evacuation from Rangoon. The route from Mandalay up to Maymyo was quite a climb, but beautiful. It was rich hunting land and once or twice an animal sprang away from the roadside as I drove up.

I had left Ismail in Mandalay; it was strange to drive alone after our months on the road together, and I kept vigilant for blocks and traps set by *dacoits*. At one point, I stopped at a curve in the road and looked down through some bare trunks to the stream below. The vegetation was dry at this time of year, but the shrubs were flowering purple; the air felt cooler after the heat and dust of Mandalay.

I drove into town, past the lovely teak and brick houses, with their lawns and country gardens. Maymyo was beset with almost continuous air alerts and bombing raids and, as I drove in, the streets had a desolate feel. I found the Lamonts staying in a simple white-painted bungalow recently vacated by a junior official whose wife had left for India. Fortunately, Eva was in when I arrived and I was pleased to see that she got into quite a flap of excitement.

'Bobby, you do have a wonderful habit of turning up just when we need you most! We knew you were all right, because Pops saw that terrible cousin of yours. Pops was harangued for about half an hour about how stupid the government is and about the dreadful inefficiencies of the authorities. Where is your cousin now? In Mandalay? Or have they posted him to the middle of the fighting zone? I bet they will and he will have a wonderful time refusing to go.'

She was still dressed in her Burmese clothes. She looked lovely, but I could sense that her brightness was forced.

She carried on, her tone dropping, 'Did you see Mummy when you were in Rangoon? She must have left when they evacuated, but we haven't heard from her at all.'

The bungalow was a simple structure with two bedrooms off a dark, central corridor. She went into one of these now to call her father. Paul Lamont came out, looking even shabbier than the last time I'd seen him, with deep sweat marks under the arms of his jacket.

'Hello, Bobby! I wondered what all the commotion was about. I must have been dozing, then I heard the girl shouting. How are you, my boy? Have you seen her mother? She wouldn't come with us, you know. Kicked up an awful fuss and there was nothing we could do.'

He sat down heavily on one of the plain wooden chairs. I explained about visiting the empty house in Rangoon. Daw Min Min's village was in the Tavoy district in the south-east of Burma but surely, I said, she must have come northwards.

'Eva doesn't want to move off until she's got her mother with her,' Lamont said, lighting up a cigarette.

*

I took Eva out to the jeep later and gave her the little scent bottle and the fan, which I'd picked up at their house in Rangoon. She turned the bottle over repeatedly in her hand without saying anything, a half-smile on her face; then, still holding it, she tucked her arm through mine and whisked the fan in front of my face jokingly.

'You're a darling. Now tell me everything that you found at home. I know you didn't want to upset Pops.'

As we walked along the main road to the bazaar, I told her about the empty streets in Rangoon, the desolation, and the burnt-out houses that I'd seen. I told her about my night in

Kokine and even something of my feelings going back there, looking out at the lake, and how the house had lost its soul. None of it seemed possible on that beautiful late afternoon in Maymyo, the smell of pine heavy in the air. And I wanted to say, 'At least you're here. I have you for now.'

I lapsed into silence and Eva tugged on my arm. Her voice lost its brightness and she walked alongside me, staring at the ground just in front of her.

'Pops is beginning to let everything get him down. I do believe that all that time he thought that Mummy would come round to the idea of leaving Rangoon. A lot of people came to realise they had to go while there was still some transport, but Mummy didn't. Now he's blaming himself for not forcing her to come with us. He's starting to brood, you know. How does he seem to you?'

She stopped and turned to face me. But before I could answer, she dropped her arm and wandered away. I sat down on a post and waited. Then she spun round suddenly, came back and continued.

'How do you think I look? Am I convincingly Burmese?' She gave a bit of a twirl, as if modelling.

There was an edge to her voice that I couldn't respond to, so I just said with a smile, 'You forget you were wearing those clothes when I saw you in Rangoon. You look good.' Then I added, 'Are you scared?'

'Not really. I'm sure that we will get away in the end if we have to. Everyone else has. But life now is so dull – apart from the wretched bombs. All you men are off fighting the Japs and there is almost nothing going on here. It's all right for the men that are still around, with the club and their endless rounds of *chota pegs*, but they are complete bores as far as I'm concerned. The wives are just as bad, Bobby, I'm telling you, and I am totally fed up with listening to them all whine on.'

We came down to the bazaar. There were still women sitting on jute sacks in the parched red dust, smoking foot-long cheroots and surrounded by bundles of acrid dried fish, and tin plates of red bananas and scarlet chillies. We wandered aimlessly along the main aisles. Rows of brass Buddhas, bundles of silks, bangles and household items were already being packed away for the day and a few hill people in their wide-brimmed straw hats – the last stragglers of the day – were making their purchases of food.

Chatting to Eva was easier than it had ever been. The touch of sadness – even her edginess – made her enormously appealing and, as we walked, I felt a great desire to touch her face. We went to the edge of the town, over the river along the Lashio road, where the thick jungle came almost to the roadside, and sat on a stone wall together with our shoulders brushing, the call of birds penetrating the stillness of the late afternoon. Eva was staring ahead and I didn't want to disturb her. I looked at the ground between my feet; the sun was still warm on my shoulders and my ears were pounding lightly. I wanted intensely to lie back and let my body melt in that heat, and to pull Eva down to me. Suddenly, some pigeons flew out of the trees nearby and we both started. Eva touched my hand.

'Will we get back again, Bobby, do you think? I mean, home? Surely the Japs won't manage to drive us right out. The Burmans and the Karens won't let them rule the country – how can they? I don't even know where we're going to stay if we get to India. We don't have any relatives there and I have no idea where my friends have ended up.'

'We just have to keep positive. That's what we're all doing, isn't it?' As I said it, I knew that I sounded ridiculous, simply parroting the official line.

Her voice became thinner. 'I don't know if we can leave without Mummy, anyway. How can I just walk out with the thought that she might be starving somewhere or killed by the Japs or *dacoits* – or anything could have happened to her with this craziness?'

I stayed with the Lamonts for the next few days while I was in Maymyo, but that was the last time Eva spoke to me about leaving Burma, and the house was almost entirely free of the talk of evacuation and routes out of the country that I met everywhere else. Food was difficult to come by, so we thought of interesting ways to eat my rations of bully beef. Eva was altogether gentler, less brittle than I had known her in Rangoon. Lamont wasn't well in with the official crowd, so there were few visitors to the bungalow. On occasions I would see evidence of Eva's flirtatious sparkle, but she seemed to be content to play endless hours of rummy or we would wind up and play the old gramophone. The days were dominated in many ways by the news bulletins but, although things were hotting up at that time around Rangoon, there was more propaganda than hard information on the radio and no one was very clear about what was happening.

*

My aunt Bea had taken a bungalow in Maymyo, and Issie's baby was expected in the next few weeks. I went over to see them later on my first evening, after I had visited the Lamonts. They had their dog, Juno, with them and she padded out to greet me when I arrived, circling round my leg, her tail gently wagging – as if reconnecting with memories of Rangoon. The constant bombing in the early mornings and the rush for cover in the trenches out in the forest were getting them down. Auntie Babs was also at home when I arrived. She was quieter than I had known her and was putting on weight, despite the difficulty in getting hold of food. There were dark circles under her eyes and, without the usual make-up, her skin looked sallow.

'Don't think for one moment that I'm hanging around here much longer, Bobby. I'm going to make sure I'm part of the airlift from Shwebo before it's too late. I'm getting it fixed up. Thank goodness for contacts in the right places!'

'What about you, Auntie?'

Aunt Bea was fidgeting with some sewing on her lap. 'Well, darling, we must wait for Issie's baby and then, if Lester can get leave, we'll all go together.'

Issie came in on cue, looking as though the baby was ready to be born any minute. Her hair was messed up, as if she had been lying down, but she seemed well – better than in Rangoon – and I said so.

'That's all very good, but I'm indescribably bored. All I can say is lucky you – able to get out and do something, and it's not as if you're doing anything particularly dangerous, is it?'

Babs looked up from filing her nails.

'You're ridiculous, Issie. Bobby has just come up from Pegu and the Japs are surrounding our troops everywhere . . .'

Issie broke in with a short laugh. 'Oh, come on, he's as likely to be killed by a bomb talking to us here as anywhere else!' She sounded irritated. 'Anyway, what I meant was that at least you can *do* something, Bobby. Of course, I'm sure you're frightfully brave like all our men.' She sighed and turned away.

The whole household was tense, but I stayed talking to Bea until her husband arrived back. Lester was in his late fifties, an easy-going man with a heavy jowl, enjoying hunting and *mahseer* fishing with his friends and colleagues. I'd never spent much time in his company, but he always welcomed me warmly enough.

*

While I was in Mandalay I had orders to transfer to Magwe in Central Burma. I usually enjoyed visiting the town, with its leafy streets and the beautiful Mya Tha Lun Pagoda dominating the bank of the Irrawaddy River. By this time the civil administration in the whole of the Magwe region had virtually broken down but, with its airfield, Magwe remained an important enough town. I left Maymyo for Mandalay on 7 March in preparation for my transfer but, when I arrived, it was only to find that my transfer was cancelled. Things were getting chaotic. First one signal was sent and then another contradicted it; it was everyone's view that we were losing our grip on Burma.

The warning had gone up on 28 February that only the last ditchers – the civilians who had stayed behind to carry out key services – would remain in Rangoon. So many, including Laura, Bea and the Lamonts had left only just in time. From what we heard, the final exodus was a stampede, with people struggling to get out because of the lack of transport. The rail link between Rangoon and Mandalay had already been cut on 22 February and now all the important installations were set alight and sabotaged so that there was nothing left of value for the Japanese. But no one was prepared for the final evacuation of Rangoon when it came. News of the final order to evacuate had arrived in Mandalay by the time I arrived on the night of 7 March and we were terribly shocked and surprised.

Once in Mandalay, my revised order was to go back down to Prome and bring up the telegraph personnel from there. We understood the Japanese had infiltrated between Tharawaddy and Prome, and everyone was very tense while we waited for instructions. Not without reason, because after 8 March our troops retired up the Prome Road and the following day the road was cut just outside Prome, with a lot of our men still on the other side. That left me pretty well exposed, because they had closed down the post and telegraph office and I ended up spending the next few days on the road between Prome and Mandalay, bringing up the staff. In one trip I had a chap – a Eurasian called Edwardes – who had been part of the last ditch operations in Rangoon and I was able to get a first-hand account of the last few hours there. Other post and telegraph personnel had gone downriver by launch and evacuated straight to Calcutta by cargo boat, but this chap had caught a lift on one of the last trucks coming up the Prome road. He described how he'd left the Rangoon telephone exchange, the telegraphic office and the Mogul Guard all in flames.

*

I didn't get back to Mandalay again until four or five days later. I went looking for Lion in the house at Aungbale on the morning I arrived. He introduced me to a stoutish man, who had a film of sweat on his face, which he wiped off with a dirty-looking handkerchief. Lion was his usual combative self.

'Lascelles here is full of a scheme for evacuating the Anglo-Burmese community to China. Come on, you can help me persuade him that it will never work. Much better that he should just get registered with one of the convoys and clear out to India with his family while he can.'

Lion coughed for a while, and his man brought in some water and a tray of strong black coffee. A bit later he continued, 'I was telling Lascelles that I've been down to the Oriental Mission trying to get a useful job. I would have thought they could have done with someone like me giving them intelligence in the north of the country or along the India-Burma route.'

I wondered how far Lion really believed anyone would take up his suggestions, or if he seriously thought that in the middle of the war he could fall back on his old role of explorer and traveller. After Lascelles left we talked about the firing of Rangoon and I told him about Edwardes' description of the destruction.

'He was saying that at Duneedaw there was black smoke billowing out from the distribution plants of Burmah Oil and the Indo-Burma Petroleum Company. It was the same thing at the refineries at Syriam and all the others. Smoke going right up into the sky – high – you could see it all around, thousands of feet. Terrible, brother!'

Lion seemed deeply affected by the stories of the evacuation and devastation of Rangoon, and he couldn't be persuaded that it had been necessary.

'We've destroyed our own city,' he said. 'What's it going to change? How much do you give me for the advancing civilisation of the British raj now?' He'd been smoking heavily since I arrived and now lit up another cigarette. 'How is it that we couldn't get to Prome before the enemy? You tell me . . . This is butchery. Stupid bunglers!'

He had raised his voice, and I could feel the blood rush into my own face. His anger had taken me off-guard and locked into some emotion of my own.

'I don't see how you can say that,' I burst out. 'Take my outfit. We've managed to shift the personnel well in advance of the army. I don't see what you're saying. You and I can't see the bigger picture anyway. It's all very well for us to point the finger. Look at this business with the asylum inmates. I was talking to a chap who met one of the psychiatrists who had come down to the Irrawaddy Flotilla Company days before they were let loose. It seems they were trying to get boats to get them up to Prome and Minbu on the river but there weren't any available. What were they to do?'

I felt tired. I didn't have the appetite to argue with Lion. I hesitated, then said, quietly, 'You see, brother, we don't always know the full story. I think it's too easy to blame the authorities, but you've got to know all the facts first, then you can blame people if you have to.'

'We don't need more facts,' Lion roared at me. 'Look at what's happening with your posting. First they tell you one thing and then another. This lot don't know which is right and which is left. I'm supposed to be going to Tharawaddy, which is pretty well the front line, and they expect me to carry on business as usual with the courts. What sort of madness is that?'

We cooled down a bit after that. I knew Lion was frustrated with his affairs, so I had breakfast with him and then went over to the telegraph office to report to Colonel Scott, and to hand over the money I had brought up from Prome. Scott was pleased with me and promised me a week's leave. Meanwhile, I found myself on my way to Meiktila within the half hour to fetch back two telegraph officials, both Burmans – one a major and the other a captain – who had taken a fortnight coming from Rangoon. I found the two men not trying to abscond, as Scott had thought, but simply taking it easy.

*

I got back to Mandalay at about three o'clock the following morning. After a brief rest at Aungbale, I went straight away to pick up my papers. The last week had been draining, so I was glad to get some leave. I realised that I desperately wanted to see Eva again and I headed up to Maymyo before lunch, leaving Ismail behind me in Mandalay. When I arrived I found

Lamont, but Eva was out. The bungalow had a depressed air about it. Paul Lamont got up slowly from his chair to greet me, a thin cigarette dangling from his lips and a glass of gin in his hand.

'Eva is out, my boy. She's down at the camp, helping with the refugees. The air raids were getting her down. I think she just needed to get out of the house. Have a drink! Come on, Bobby, have a drink . . . Majid!'

Majid came in quietly. 'Good morning, sahib.'

I smiled at him and asked for a beer. I was surprised at what Lamont was saying. The last time I'd seen them, Eva hadn't mentioned any intention to help out, although I knew that the camps were in a desperate condition and enlisting volunteers. It was the same situation as in Mandalay: there was an increasing mass of evacuees in Maymyo and the Evacuation Commissioner was responsible for moving them to stage camps further north, but the situation was in chaos.

I found Eva down at the refugee camp. She was no longer in a *longyi*, but instead was wearing a plain skirt and blouse. She walked outside the camp with me.

'Did Pops tell you I'm spending my time here now? What do you think? I just couldn't sit around the house any more, Bobby, hiding from the enemy. Might as well be useful, don't you agree? I'm helping to sort out food and drink for the refugees; you know, most of them don't have anything. It's terrible – some haven't eaten for days by the time they get here and then, poor things, there's really nothing for them once they *are* here. The children are suffering. I don't know how they're going to survive. Actually, we are losing them all the time.'

'It's the same in all the camps,' I said. 'Shocking.' I had seen the conditions when I'd left the telegraph girls in holding camps over the last several weeks. I had always suspected that Eva was stronger than she appeared. 'Don't you mind?' I added. I could smell the camps on my way into the town and as I'd got close the stench was appalling.

'Of course I mind, Bobby! Nearly all the sweepers have disappeared, so no one is using the latrines which have been set up. We have to clean our own at home now, you know. The cook has gone and Majid is leaving us as well. You're going to stay, aren't you?'

I nodded.

'Is Ismail with you?'

'No.'

'That's all right.' Eva smiled faintly. 'You can be our cook, then, because you can see I'm too busy.' She took my hand in both of hers.

I was disappointed that I wouldn't be seeing Eva during the day, but I was proud of her, too. The war had an effect on people.

*

In the event, I was able to spend some time with my father. He had been moving around the country on his insurance business and was staying in the *dak* bungalow in Maymyo for a few days as there was no room at Aunt Bea's. Issie had just had her baby and the landlady had moved other tenants into a part of the house, as their own bungalow had been bombed. My father was travelling with Ba Yee, who mothered him, and somehow managed to keep his suits and shirts pressed, so that he looked for all the world as if he had just stepped out of his office in Phayre Street. There was still a strain between us but it was a different one, and had to do with my being in the military and my father at a loose end. He didn't see his insurance business as part of the war effort, so maybe he felt rejected in some way. Certainly, without the Family around him he seemed less powerful, adrift. He was subject to mood changes – always part of his personality but now more evident – and at times he was subdued, almost apologetic in his manner. He was anxious to get out of Burma if he couldn't be useful. When Lion came up from Mandalay they spent evenings discussing for how long the Tamu route would be closed and alternative ways out of Burma, much in the way that they had poured over maps of the China-Burma border in the evenings at Kokine before one of their expeditions together back in the twenties and thirties.

Generally, Lion was in poor spirits and he and my father engaged in a crazy emotional seesaw, with one of them bursting with optimism and a new proposal, while the other would be sunk in depression.

One afternoon my father pointed a finger at me as I came into the house and said he was hatching a new plan. Later in the evening he was excited, the three of us sitting by the kerosene lamp in the bedroom of the *dak* bungalow. He talked of his intention to be useful to the war effort and about using his jungle and tracking experience and his knowledge of the hill country.

'I told you my wandering days were not over, my boy!'

He didn't offer any further explanation, so I looked at Lion; but my cousin just took the pipe out of his mouth with an air of exasperation and went over to his jacket to find more tobacco.

Turning round, he proclaimed, '*The universe is resounding with the music of wings . . .* something, something . . .' He petered out, then started again, '*Oh, homeless bird, which flies day and night . . . not here, not here.*'

'What's that?' I asked.

'A poem, dear boy. A poem!' And he knocked his pipe on the cane table.

The two of them were becoming increasingly enigmatic. I realised that as the war drew close it was somehow drawing a line between what they'd been – a certainty about their standing and the familiar trappings of their lives – and a future that looked increasingly unknown. In fact, I picked up hints that Lion was deep in some financial trouble, but he didn't tell me about it and it was not the sort of information my father, if he had it, would ever have willingly shared with me.

All three of us were due to return to Mandalay. Lion left a few days before us, but I stayed on to drive my father down with Ba Yee. My father was quite animated; it seemed that his new plan was to join a commando on the northern border with China. But my thoughts were elsewhere. I had received another posting to Magwe, and my first business was to report and receive my orders.

Once we left the hills, the drive was hot and dusty. Mandalay was a depressing sight. The town hadn't suffered greatly from its bombing in February, but the streets were filthy, with piles of rubbish left to rot at the sides of the roads. My father wanted to be left at the post office and, as we drove down 78th Street past the railway station, there were crowds of evacuees about. I reported in to the telegraph office to find that the RAF was abandoning Magwe after the bombing of the airfield there and they would be going to Lashio. What this meant for my own posting was completely uncertain, but I was still required to go to Magwe to evacuate the staff.

When I arrived at the Aungbale house – 'the Shack,' my cousin called it – Lion was out and Murthi, his servant, gave me dinner. When Lion came in he looked pretty awful: his lightweight jacket was crumpled and his official black trousers dusty, his tie loosely knotted and unevenly tied. He told a lengthy story about attempts to sell his car, and I guessed that part of his intensity about it had to do with the tricky financial situation that he was in. When he sat down to dinner I told him that my father was trying to join a commando, and he threw down his knife and groaned.

'Now I've heard everything!' he said. He drew his hands down over his face, elbows on the table, looking up at me through his fingers in an exaggerated gesture of despair. I shrugged my shoulders and changed the conversation.

'Tell me what's happening in Mandalay. It looks as if it's going from bad to worse.'

'What do you think, Bobby? The administration is at breaking point. Quite simply! We have more and more civil officers here in Mandalay coming up from the south, but they can't seem to cope with the problem. The thing is that the Tamu road is still closed while they complete the metalling, and they don't want it clogged up with civilian refugees if the military have to retreat suddenly.'

'So how the hell are the remaining refugees going to get out?'

'That, my boy, is a good question. What *is* going to happen to them? They don't have any priority by air, as you know. For example, they say there are nearly a hundred thousand refugees here in Mandalay right now, and there is smallpox and cholera breaking out. It's disgraceful.'

I was finding the atmosphere with Lion intense and oppressive, and decided to put my bedding down somewhere else that night. So I left Mandalay without seeing my father again, heading back south to Myingyan with Ismail after breakfast the next morning. From there my destination was Magwe, on the banks of the Irrawaddy, to carry out staff evacuation. Two or three miles outside Mandalay we passed a knot of villagers on the roadside. They held up their meagre produce for sale, waving it at us – a few bunches of red bananas and two or three dusty-looking bottles of toddy.

12

LION

March and April 1942

After my father gave me Lion's diary, I tried to put together what he'd already told me about those frantic days in February and March 1942 with Lion's entries for that time. By March, many of the families forced out of Rangoon, unable to leave by boat or plane, were pushed northwards, many now crowding into Mandalay – Lion and Robert among them – as the heat rose and the town became insanitary and disease ridden. The government itself had moved to Maymyo, set in the cooler hills above Mandalay. Lion seemed set on pulling whatever rank he had to get the official leave that would allow him to evacuate.

Chrissie S.

Tuesday, 3 March, Mandalay

Robert and I listen to the radio, but nothing is being reported from the Sittang front. The situation seems to be unchanged. Are they holding back the news of the fact that Pegu has been taken? It's quite likely. We have all completely lost confidence in the radio news. Every government department is working badly and it would be extraordinary if the radio section were working efficiently.

The heat is unbearable! I took Robert for a drive around the Fort to see the damage that has been done by the bombs. The Upper Burma Club is now a complete wreck. There were about fifty bombs dropped in the Fort, but the one in the Club was the only effective one.

Bobby came over in his jeep. He told us all about his experiences since leaving Lower Burma. He said that he spent two days in my house in Pegu and was turned out by the military. He then went to Waw on duty and escaped being machine gunned by

146

taking shelter in a ditch. Our house at Kokine had been entered and partly looted and Bobby was a bit emotional about it. It looks as if our own military had been there and not the Burmese looters. The latter would have made a complete job of it.

Bobby left for Maymyo late this evening after depositing some of his stuff with us here.

Wednesday, 4 March, Mandalay

I bought a Morris 8 car for 800 rupees this morning. It needed some minor repairs and I left my Chev for repairs as well.

The news through the radio is very scanty. The situation on the Sittang front is unchanged but there is patrol activity around Pegu. This news must surely be the prelude to an announcement that Pegu has fallen. Toungoo was blitzed a few days ago, particularly the bazaar and the railway quarter, and there were heavy casualties inflicted. It's the same story in Pyinmana. But without newspapers, it's impossible to keep track of events.

Friday, 6 March, Maymyo

I arrived in Maymyo last night with Robert. We lost our way over and over again, which was infuriating with petrol being so severely rationed. I put up in B's flat – which turned out to be a filthy place covered in dust and papers strewn about in indescribable confusion. Some acquaintance of B's stole some of my petrol after I had refused his request to give him some. He was a complete stranger to me and I didn't see why I should give him any as I had just enough for my own needs.

I met Gerald Bourne today in the Court House. He's been put in charge of distributing food. He displayed his usual vagueness. And he asked me again about going to Shwebo. I said I was disinclined to do any more judicial work and I asked him whom I should see about the executive work that I wanted to do. He said he didn't know – all the departments seem to work independently of each other now. And even parts of one department don't seem to know where the other parts are or what they're doing. There is a complete and disgraceful breakdown of the administration.

I heard that Issie went to Shwebo in a convoy of about 60 or 70 pregnant women who were to have been flown over from Shwebo to Chittagong. They all went to Shwebo in cars but found that no arrangements had been made for them. They had been told to bring enough food for one meal only, and then suddenly found out that they would have to wait for at least three days and then probably be taken over two by two – which meant a further wait of possibly weeks. Issie is now back in Maymyo and will have the baby there.

Sunday, 8 March, Maymyo and Mandalay

Bobby left for Mandalay yesterday following news of his transfer to Magwe as Liaison Officer for Posts and Telegraphs. However, when we arrived at Mandalay at 7 pm we found that his transfer had been cancelled and he is now ordered to go to Prome to bring back the telegraph personnel from there. It seems the Japs have infiltrated between Tharrawaddy and Prome, and the Prome crowd have got jittery. There is to be no posts and telegraphs office at all – which is a strange arrangement considering that the other government offices are all still functioning there and the town has not yet been evacuated.

I had a letter from Ghose yesterday about our little financial arrangement, which was very depressing. I was even more depressed by a visit from Hla Pe today chasing up the other loan. When shall I be able to shake him off? I gave him the February instalment as it seems he didn't receive the money order that I sent from Pegu.

Monday, 9 March, Mandalay

The District and Sessions Judge here is Gledhill, and I went to his house in the afternoon. Mrs P was there, a domineering sort and ultra-bulldoggish and won't hear a thing against the government. On the other hand, she is off by plane to India tomorrow, starting from Shwebo, and grumbled because she couldn't be taken by car to Shwebo but instead had to go in a refugee train. Her husband is a nice fellow and very quietly pointed out that it would be wrong to motor because of the petrol shortage.

There is news that the demolition squad have dynamited government buildings, the powerhouse, the post office and various industrial installations in Rangoon. The other news is that the Japs have reached the Prome Road near the Hmawbi air base, just north of Rangoon. How did they get there? What about our tanks? It appears that the road was cleared of the Japs by our planes and there was no contact between our troops and the enemy troops. The Japanese radio is claiming that their forces are occupying Rangoon.

Tuesday, 10 March, Mandalay

I went to Gledhill's again this morning and met Mrs T there and her husband, whom I don't like. He talked about the shortage of coolie labour and seemed to think that armed force should have been used to press them to work. An absolutely monstrous suggestion, probably the effect of putting a military uniform on a civilian of the academic type.

At 2 pm we received the following Burma Broadcast from Maymyo: RANGOON HAS BEEN EVACUATED BY ALL MILITARY AND CIVILIAN POPULATION.

It's now clear a scorched earth policy has been rigorously applied and the whole of Rangoon is blazing from end to end. I can't believe that all the civilian population has had a chance to leave. Colonel F was sent only the day before to collect evacuees from the asylum and bring them away, and he was given lorries and a hundred gallons of petrol so that he could do it. We were both at the petrol pump at Maymyo together.

People are saying that only lepers and beggars are left in Rangoon, starving and searching for food. Rangoon has become a city of death. And yet the Governor is taking credit to himself – or rather the government is – proclaiming that the destruction of the fine city of Rangoon has compared well as far as the scorched earth policy is concerned with the destruction of the Dneiper Dam by the retreating Red Army last year. And I suppose a large number of people will get decorations over this sad business. Yes, destroy Rangoon after proper evacuation, but there was no evacuation, only an utterly disgraceful stampede of those who were well enough off to own, borrow or hire motors and other forms of transport.

It was announced on the radio that the Prome Road has definitely been cut off near Hmawbi and there has been heavy fighting and many casualties there. It's also been admitted on the Burma Radio that the Japs have landed by sea near the China Bakir River, immediately south of Rangoon. Our air forces went to intercept but were too late as the Japs had already landed. This means that the whole delta is in their hands – in other words that they have Lower Burma. Upper Burma, when?

I forgot to mention that I learned that the commanding officer of the Duke of Wellington's was murdered by Burmese *thakins* after he had swum across the Sittang. Nine battalions and four batteries were left on the wrong side of the Sittang after we had blown up the bridge. There is just blunder after blunder, and yet the military behave as if they were conquering heroes.

Thursday, 12 March, Maymyo

I arrived in Maymyo yesterday with Robert and taking Ba Yee with us. We went out in a phaeton and visited Lester and Bea. Issie had her baby two days ago, a daughter.

I called in on the Oriental Mission at Comaresk. The sort of work they want their men to do is to go behind the Japanese lines and harry the enemy. I am naturally considered too old for this sort of job. I suggested that I could report on the routes between Burma and India, but was told that that was Intelligence work and outside the scope of the Mission. So there it is – an end to all my plans.

With the High Court operating from Maymyo, I called on Bourne at the control room. He told me that he had just sent a wire to Mandalay informing me of my transfer to Tharawaddy, which is practically our front line in Lower Burma. It seemed that the Tharawaddy judge had bolted to Kalaw. I went and saw Dunkley about precise instructions. He met me with a sour face, thinking I had come to wrangle out of his order of transfer, and changed somewhat when he realised that I was fully prepared to carry out the orders given to me. He gave me a note on a plain piece of paper stating that Mr LB Hennessey was on transfer to Tharawaddy as District and Sessions Judge and that he should be given sufficient petrol for the journey. As if anyone would take any notice of the chit!! The High Court judges seem to think their least wishes are still law here. The chit is absolutely worthless, although I didn't want to annoy him by telling him so.

My instructions are to take over and hear appeals by the courts that are still functioning! I fail to understand how Dunkley, now at the head of the High Court, is unable to realise that there is not the remotest possibility of the courts carrying on as usual at Tharawaddy. I managed to get an understanding that if they're not functioning, I'm to report on the situation and evacuate the judges and give them and their staff three months' salary, and then return here.

To Bea and Lester's after seeing Dunkley. There was only Babs at home and she tells me that Burma Radio announced at 2 pm that Tharawaddy had been occupied by the Japs, although this was not yet officially confirmed. Yet at 5 pm I was again given instructions to proceed to Tharawaddy. What a comic opera! Surely it was Dunkley's duty to have ascertained first what the situation was at Tharrawaddy before arranging to gazette me to the district as judge. But High Court judges live on too high an altitude to take notice of such minor details as these.

It also seems that the Burmese have been joining up with the Japs in Lower Burma. Meanwhile, our reinforcements from India have been turned back on the grounds that there weren't enough food supplies for them. Some troopships have apparently paid two visits to Rangoon with the same troops. So that's it. Now all our hopes must be centred on the Chinese.

I went for a pleasant drive to the lake with Robert in a phaeton *gharry*. Robert says he will come with me to Tharrawaddy. He's a great sport. I met with Bourne again accidentally outside the Swiss confectionary. He told me that the Japs had not occupied Tharrawaddy but that a rebellion had broken out there, which in my mind is much worse.

Friday, 13 March, Maymyo

I met a young captain at the club who had swum the Sittang after the battle there. I also met Healy, the war correspondent for the *Daily Mirror*. He's an interesting man and willing to talk, but he was constantly interrupted by Mrs S, who kept butting in with her own petty experiences or with comments made in an annoyingly dogmatic tone of voice.

Healy was at Pegu on 7 March when the Japs broke through. He had been in France during the evacuation and was in the thick of it in other places in Europe in the present war but, according to him, none of his former experiences could compare with the fighting around Pegu. The eerie part of it was that though our men knew they were being surrounded, and the fire of machine guns, bombs etc all grew more and more intense, no Japs could be seen. It was this fighting against an invisible foe that made the experience so sinister. It seems that a reward has been offered to the first soldier that sees a Jap. An apocryphal story no doubt, but it does indicate that the Japanese are our superiors in jungle warfare, though we thought they'd never be any good at it. Our troops were cut off at Pegu and only just escaped being taken.

Now the fighting is going on in the Taikkyi area. Healy told me about meeting a whole crowd of Indians – men, women and children refugees – near Pyinmana. They were a pathetic sight and begging for water. There you have the victims of that damned 'stay-put' policy. Healy was at a conference at Government House last evening. The Governor told him that 'the civil administration is done for'. This is hardly news to anybody resident in Burma at this moment. It's a disgraceful collapse of the whole rotten bureaucratic system.

At every European house you visit you find whisky and gin served as usual. I heard that twenty tons of essential drugs had been left behind in Rangoon, but that alcohol had been brought away, some in specially chartered launches. What about all the rice left in Lower Burma? No one seems to have had the foresight to have removed stocks to Upper Burma where it's needed.

Sunday, 15 March, Mandalay

I arrived in Mandalay mid-morning yesterday. Everyone seems to regard my posting to Tharawaddy as a sign of lunacy on the part of the government. We hear that the government has opened the Mogaung Kamaing Road to civilians, but I wonder if it's true. It seems contrary to their criminal policy of keeping people shut up here in Burma until the moment comes for a stampede.

Bobby arrived from Prome today. I was very glad to see him and relieved to know that he is safe. He did his work satisfactorily and brought away the telegraph staff and also 27,000 rupees which he made over to the authorities here. He seems to enjoy his work and mercifully for him he doesn't realise how the government has let everybody down. He was very pleased to hear that I had seen his commission gazetted in the Burma Gazette. He was obviously worried at not having been gazetted earlier, but the boy is doing well and I'm sure will get his captaincy soon.

I forgot to mention that yesterday I met the man who was deputy commissioner at Mergui at the time of the evacuation from there. He confirmed the story about some Indian Public Works Department clerks being refused places on the cargo boat, the *Harvey Adamson*, which was taking away European and Anglo-Indian refugees from there. God knows what the fate of those poor devils was, but can they be blamed for being bitter about their treatment and for becoming antagonised against the British?

Tuesday, 17 March, Maymyo

I arrived in Maymyo yesterday evening. Bobby had got here before us in his jeep on five days leave. There was an air raid for about half an hour in the early hours. C turned up to put up at the flat completely blotto and with damaged lips and knee due to a fall at the club after a heavy binge. The smell of whisky from him was quite nauseating. This gives the final blow to any lingering temptation I have had to find solace in the bottle again. It's almost seven months to the day since I touched any alcohol.

Thursday, 19 March, Maymyo

We heard on the radio today that the Japs had reached Tharrawaddy on the West Road.

I went to the Home Secretary's office to find that a letter had been written to Prome to the Commissioner to find out whether a sessions judge could function at Tharrawaddy – and this is when it is known that the military are in occupation of the town! It's just red tape of the most fatuous kind. I said it would take a considerable time for a reply to get here by post. In fact, it's doubtful whether it will get here at all now that the Post Office is in such a mess; I anticipate at least a fortnight's wait. I said that in the circumstances, since it was immaterial where I waited, I would move to Maymyo. I couldn't stand the infernal heat and dust of Mandalay any longer.

I drove down to Mandalay. Robert stayed behind with Ba Yee as he's coming down the day after tomorrow with Bobby. I had a rotten evening and it was most depressing. I didn't have any dinner; I tried to make shift with a tin of spaghetti, but then didn't eat it. This house and the street it's in is a desolate place – dusty, smelly and slummy.

Friday, 20 March, Mandalay

I slacked in the house in my Shan pyjamas until after lunch. I forgot to mention that my main cause of depression last night was a letter from the Chief Justice, enclosing a complaint from

Mrs Ghose about my delay in repaying the loan given me. The CJ's letter is a very decent one, but still, my real financial position is now disclosed to him. It's a truly awful mess, but I will steer my way through, please God!

Harry turned up in the afternoon, full of his experiences bringing up the wounded from Lower Burma in the Irrawaddy Flotilla launches. I took him with me to call on Payton, who had practised at the bar with me in the early days, and had just turned up with Tun Tin by boat. Ba U was full of indignation about the breakdown of the administration. I allowed him to let off steam for a while. He told me that the Chief Justice was maintaining a diary and collecting material for an indictment of the government. This afternoon we had news from the Burma Radio that our troops have retired from Tharrawaddy. So I haven't had long to wait for the solution to the question of whether I should be going there or not. And now, what next?

Sunday, 22 March, Mandalay

Yesterday I spent half the morning drafting a letter to the Chief Justice about the Ghose matter, but I couldn't put my mind to it.

All around there are examples of the absurdity of human behaviour. Yesterday I saw Adler, who says that he feels it in his bones that Mandalay will soon be bombed again, and he wants to get off to Myitkyina to do some *mahseer* fishing! In the evening I called on Mrs T, who is as calm and placid as ever, but there seems something fatuous and irritating in this attitude just now. In her case it springs from her unshakeable faith in God.

There was a very high wind last night and some rain. It was a curious sort of night, but it seems to have made the atmosphere somewhat clearer today.

In his essay on circles, Emerson omitted to mention one important category – those aimless circles in which officials move when an administration has broken down, as in Burma just now. And also those tight little circles of self-centredness into which people withdraw during a crisis like this.

I visited Gledhill who was very woolly-headed. His brain seems to have gone. He said that from what he had heard of the finances of Burma, he had made up his mind to scrape together every half-anna and remit the money to his wife in India. It looks as if the government are on the verge of bankruptcy and both funds and pensions are in jeopardy. And what about our jobs?

When I got back to the house I found that Bobby was back again having dinner. He couldn't go straight on to Magwe as news had just come in that as a result of the bombing on Saturday, I think, the RAF were abandoning the aerodrome at Magwe and going to Lashio. A depressing piece of news. This leaves Yenangyaung unprotected and also the whole of Central Burma. It looks as if we intend to try to hold only the upper part of Burma.

There are reports of the torture of Gloucester Regiment prisoners by the Japanese at Hmawbi. Flaying them alive and exposing them in the sun. Robert has almost fixed up to join a commando. But he forgets not only his age, but also the fact that the Burma of today isn't the Burma of his past. He used to go out shooting amongst a friendly people; now many of those people have become open enemies.

Tuesday, 24 March, Mandalay

I went to see about the Chev without success. Harry arrived with his luggage and his dog. Bobby left for Myingyan immediately after breakfast. From Myingyan he is going to Magwe to evacuate the staff there.

I called on Payton, the Chief Secretary, and had a most unsatisfactory interview. He said I must proceed to Magwe without delay and wouldn't let me fit in a visit to see the Chief Justice though I told him that it was on a matter of vital importance to me.

I arrived at Mandalay at about 8 o'clock in the evening to find a stinker of a letter waiting for me from Ghose; the whole thing is very depressing.

Wednesday, 25 March, Mandalay

I've had a thoroughly tiring and depressing day. First of all I went to court to pay in the balance from the Pegu Treasury. While I was there an air-raid alarm sounded but I stayed in Gledhill's chambers and carried on chatting with him. Three Japanese planes passed and repassed far overhead.

In the end I didn't pay the money into the Treasury as I couldn't complete the paperwork. As always, further particulars were needed.

I then spent time trying to requisition a car and got a Chev RC 1900. I was rushed into accepting it, and it proved to be a bad machine straight away. The self-starter won't work, the brakes are bad and so on. We struggled with it in the sun for a couple of hours and then returned it feeling quite done in for the day. I've now had a Renault picked out for me, so I'll see to that tomorrow.

The radio news is that the Japs are above Toungoo now and have taken the aerodrome just north of it. The fighting is below Prome and the Chinese are surrounded in Toungoo. The Chinese complain of a lack of air support. I wonder if the route to Magwe is under martial law. If this is true, there isn't much chance of my functioning there as a civil judge.

I forgot to mention that while I was at Maymyo there was confirmation that a couple of thousand Indian coolies were left behind in Rangoon. There was no room left on the steamers for the evacuation and they had to be kept off from boarding at the point of revolvers. It's a dreadful, tragic business for which the government should be impeached.

I turned in early and very depressed – chiefly about Ghose's letter.

Sunday, 29 March, Mandalay and left for Magwe

We were very busy packing and getting the Renault ready, which we camouflaged with brown Irrawaddy mud. We got away at last at the end of the afternoon and arrived in Meiktila at about 6.30 pm. I didn't meet the Deputy Commissioner tonight as he hadn't returned from tennis before I had to get to the Circuit

House for dinner. I slept at the public works bungalow as the Circuit House was full of military.

Monday, 30 March, Left Meiktila for Magwe

Today I had a long chat with the DC at his house in Meiktila, and it's obvious that he had Burmese sympathies rather than for the British. He strenuously denied that any Indian coolies had been left behind in Rangoon although I said that I had the word of eye-witnesses. He had heard about my appointment to Tharrawaddy and told me that a story had gone around that I was sent to Tharrawaddy as a punishment for having run away from Pegu prematurely. I protested vigorously, and he was surprised to hear that I had left only after the evacuation of Pegu. The utter madness and malice of people! This more than anything else now sickens me of the whole damned business, and I am more anxious than ever to get away on leave. As far as I'm concerned, let the bloody country stew in its own mess. But it's the poor Indians who are going to suffer, and it's too awful to think about it.

I had a disastrous journey. About 12 miles from Kyaupadaung and 35 miles from Yenangyaung I had to abandon the car after stripping it of as much as possible. Major Burnett came to my rescue and tried to tow me but the rope wouldn't hold. I decided eventually to leave the car, knowing that it would probably be stripped bare as a picked bone within half an hour of our going. Even before we started we saw one of the vultures or jackals approaching warily. That reminds me that I saw an actual jackal crossing the road – the first time that I've seen one of those animals in Burma.

Tuesday, 31 March, Yenangyaung and Magwe

I left for Magwe in the police mail bus, a sorry old Burmese bus which was absolutely crowded with passengers. I endured a most painful journey to Magwe, especially the latter part, along a corrugated road which made the old bus vibrate through and through and bump around although going at about ten miles per hour. The driver accelerated past the aerodrome where there were about thirty of our machines destroyed in the last raid – a sad sight.

Before reaching Magwe I met Bobby in his jeep on a trip into Yenangyaung for the day. I gave him the glare glasses we talked about and arranged to meet him in the evening. Not long after my arrival there was an air raid and a bomb dropped on the aerodrome. I had been caught in the middle of my bath so had to take shelter in the trench near the kitchen wrapped in only a towel. There was a second air raid in the afternoon of shorter duration. Afterwards, I slept on the floor on the veranda.

Wednesday, 1 April, Magwe . . . Minbu

The Commissioner, Swithenbank, is here and looks very worn out, and his gloom and silences are awesome. His manner with me was constrained and abrupt, so I gave up putting myself out to talk to him. Frankly he's an infinite bore, a wet blanket and devitaliser of the first order. McCracken, the First Secretary, didn't turn up until the afternoon, a dour Scot with very much the idea that the judiciary are also under him. It was a very unsatisfactory interview in the course of which, in talking about the possible evacuation of Minbu, he said we would take orders from the DC as to when to go. I said that at Pegu I had been instructed to use my own discretion. He said he knew nothing about Pegu and it didn't seem wise to argue with him. I must get out of this place at all costs. After my spell in this division is over, it will be 'Goodbye Burma!' I won't hesitate for one moment to ask for leave.

Bobby left this morning and hopes to be back on Saturday or Sunday. I've asked him to bring back my jeep.

At the end of the afternoon I left for Minbu, taking the ferry across the Irrawaddy. It was an Indian launch, the *Koh-i-Nohr*, and we had a guard of a couple of policemen. At Minbu, the Deputy Superintendent of Police asked me to dinner. He was quite tight and dinner didn't start until about 10.30. He and his stable companion both talked interminably and when the DSP was talking, the Captain went to sleep. Both of them are bores of the profoundest kind.

Thursday, 2 April, Minbu

I took charge first thing in the afternoon. Some of the subordinate judges called on me but there were no cases.

The radio news is that some 4,000 fifth columnists led by Japanese officers are marching up the west bank of the Irrawaddy from Shwedaung. This is bad news. Prome is not yet taken but there is heavy fighting seven miles away.

There was a Jap plane overhead but no raid.

Good Friday, 3 April, Minbu

Japanese planes came over twice but they were only single planes and there was no raid. The news is that the general evacuation of non-essential personnel was to begin at once. It's been a very short term of office for me but I'm more than glad to be able to go. I went for a walk with some others up to the mud volcanoes, which were very interesting, but when we got back we had radio news that Mandalay had been bombed. I was enormously depressed at this news and wonder how Robert, Bobby and Harry are.

I learn from the doctor that the mental patients transferred from the asylum in Rangoon are to be left behind though the warders are to be evacuated. I asked how the inmates were going to fend for themselves. The answer was that there will be enough food left for them for six months. Apparently no one has considered the absolute certainty that they will be robbed of their food. There are a few (I think about half a dozen) dangerous lunatics among them and I asked how they would be dealt with. I leave the answer blank but it is indelibly printed on my mind.

I asked about the ordinary patients. It seems there are very few of them; they can't be evacuated so they are going to be taken to the asylum and left there with the mental patients. My God, has the world gone mad? I have a bad fit of depression and am going to bed with a heavy heart.

Saturday, 4 April, Minbu

I had a tiresome day closing down the courts and signing pay bills. I drew my own pay and one month's advance.

After breakfast there was a droning of planes and an air raid on Magwe town in the afternoon. I was alone in the Circuit trench at first and later joined the Circuit House butler and his family and other servants in their hideout among the roots of a big tree behind the servants' quarters.

I spent the rest of the afternoon choosing a car. Finally, on my second visit to the military police lines where the cars were parked, I took a Morris 14.

I went back to the Court House to find a deputation of judges and clerks anxious for counter-signatures to bills for another month's advance pay, apparently authorised by the finance department. A telegram arrived from the Chief Justice saying that he couldn't give me casual leave. I returned home depressed.

Sunday, 5 April, Minbu, Magwe . . . Popa

It's been a hell of a day. I had arranged to leave Minbu by the 8 am ferry but it left a quarter of an hour early and I had to wait till 11.30 for the next crossing and this very nearly didn't come off as the military had commandeered the boat to take a captain and twenty men to Minhla. Fortunately, owing to some delay they cried off this arrangement.

I had breakfast with Po Kha, who is the assistant judge. He has a charming, hospitable wife, Sino-Burmese I think by her appearance, and nice intelligent kids. Mrs Po Kha is stout and middle-aged and gave me things of her own cooking, insisting that I take a small bag of her home-made toffee, some eggs and a tin of bully beef.

There was a long wait at the landing place and a slight drizzle that cooled the air. All my clerical staff came to see me off.

In Magwe I had a sticky sort of interview with McCracken, in which I had to use all my powers of tactfulness. He asked me straight away who gave me permission to leave Minbu, oblivious of the fact that under the ordinance I am free to make my headquarters anywhere I choose in my division and that in any case I'm not under him or the Deputy Commissioner. He seemed to think I was, taking the view that I was an essential, which of course is wrong. He's a dour old Scot of the righteous, narrow type. I thought it wisest not to argue with him as he talked of cancelling the notice to evacuate me, and certainly could do it.

The Deputy Commissioner helped me to pack the jeep and was altogether decent and pleasant – a very capable DC, I should think. He advised me to go at top speed past the aerodrome, but I hardly needed his advice. I got caught at the edge of the aerodrome in a convoy of military lorries and armoured cars all driven by Indian soldiers. I tooted my horn and fortunately with that, and possibly because they took me for a military officer, I got past them and then pushed on to Yenangyaung at an average of 45 miles an hour.

Monday, 6 April, Popa . . . Mandalay

I travelled from Yenangyaung to Popa last night, some forty miles. I'm glad I did as it's a charming spot and I needed the rest after a very arduous and trying day. I spent the night in a delightful *dak* bungalow. It was really restful with a lovely little garden in front and a swimming pool.

At Meiktila, the DC had a few words with me as I waited for my petrol. He altered my petrol permit from eight to four gallons. Bah! Meiktila had been bombed on Saturday and I could see the results of the raid as I left town. It was a dreadfully hot drive from Meiktila to Mandalay. At Kyaukse I called on the DC to ask for petrol. He said he would give me some, but he only gave me about a bottleful although I'm sure he had a lot with him. I saw him whispering to his son when he asked him to fetch petrol for me – obviously instructing him to give only a little.

I reached Mandalay in the early evening. I wasn't prepared for the scene of desolation and death. There is a smell of dead bodies, there are starving dogs roaming about, the houses, trees and telegraph wires are all down in the uttermost confusion. Practically the whole town from the edge of the Civil Lines to right beyond the railway station is in ruins and has been devastated by fire as well.

Robert and Harry were at the Shack at Aungbale 31st Street. Bobby was there as well. The house is dreadfully insanitary as the closets haven't been cleaned out for two days. The sweeper hasn't turned up to clean them since the air raid.

Tuesday, 7 April, Mandalay

I spent the day at Mandalay as there was no petrol available to go to Maymyo. I went to the post office with Robert to look for letters for us from the Family, but it was an impossible task.

We had the wildest night I've ever experienced. A storm broke out with lightning, thunder and some rain, and the whole sky lit up with a sinister light from a fresh fire that broke out near the station. It looked as if nature was at her most diabolical as well; the utter indifference of nature to man is clear to me.

Wednesday, 8 April, Mandalay . . . Maymyo

I couldn't get petrol at any place so Bobby gave me some from his army drum. I packed up to go to Maymyo, abandoning all but the bare essentials of my journey to India in case I was allowed to go. Robert said he'd come up with me and bike back. It ended up in a big row with him merely because the bike couldn't be carried in the way that he wanted it done, that is, with Murthi sitting on top of the pile of luggage and hanging on to it. He got huffed and said hurtful things typical of how he was in the old days. In the end we patched it up in a sort of way, but he and I cannot leave together. I have had enough of being bossed about and I don't intend to put up with it any more.

About three miles from Maymyo we stopped on account of an air raid – Maymyo was bombed at noon. We got in about 1.30 and I dropped Robert off. I told him to give up the idea of cycling back and suggested that he should take the jeep and

Bobby could bring it up again for me. But Robert was obstinate as usual.

I called on Bourne in his office and he was as good-natured, but as vague and useless, as ever. He suggested I should take leave and I said I would see Dunkley about it. I later met Dunkley at the club with his wife. He also suggested that I go on leave and said he would recommend it because I deserved it as I had had a strenuous time. Dunkley and his wife are off by air on Sunday!

I put in my leave application. There were two air alarms and I took Bea and family in the jeep to the jungles about three miles outside Maymyo until the alarm was over.

In the evening I visited E at Craddock Court. He was maudlin with gin and was very dismal and pessimistic about the chances of getting out of Burma at all.

The second bombing of Mandalay took place yesterday. It took place before Robert got back there. I understand that this time they finished completely with the station and they also bombed the Fort badly. I hear that the Civil Lines remain intact.

Friday, 10 April, Maymyo

An alarm went up at about 10 am. I took Bea and family out to the jungles in the jeep until it was over. There wasn't any bombing.

After I had breakfast there was another alarm just as I was on my way to the Treasury to get my pay bill cashed. I took shelter in the trench at the Forestry Department rest house. I went on to the Treasury after the raid and got my pay bill passed, although it wasn't cashed till late in the afternoon, after a lot of difficulty. I visited the Home Secretary's office and found that my application had gone up to the Governor.

I met Weymss and he said I was just the man for a job as liaison officer with the Chinese Army. They are on the lookout for suitable men, and Weymss was going to mention my name. This would have meant saying goodbye to my leave, so I went to Weymss's house to tell him I was definitely not taking the job.

In the evening I went for a cycle ride to the club. There I met a host of officers – a boozy lot with all sorts of moustaches and silly unintelligent faces. No wonder things are going badly for us.

Bea had a heart attack but got over it quickly.

Sunday, 12 April, Maymyo, Mandalay, Maymyo

I had a curt letter from Robert saying that he's off tomorrow to Pakkoku and will try to make his way to India via Falam and Aijal. Not a word about my car, the things in the house or what he has done with his petrol, so desperately needed. Well, that's that.

I caught a lift to Mandalay to see about the car. Mandalay after the second bombing is a terrible sight, with horses dead in the road, wide areas in complete ruin, fires still raging and all the streets and houses deserted. It's a graveyard. In the whole length of B Road I saw one solitary soldier. The whole town is given over to the Chinese Army. We visited two Armenian doctors in the Fort who say the British garrison is leaving. Everything is packed up but the destination is not known yet.

On our way to Mandalay we visited the Anglo-Indian refugee camp at Shwezayan at the 14th Mile. It was a pitiful sight. We met Lascelles and his family packed into the bus ready to go to Myohung en route to Meiktila for evacuation by air. It seems about 150 refugees are taken off daily and they expect to clear the camp by Wednesday. There is a sentry at the entrance and the refugees are treated like convicts and are not allowed out of the camp precincts.

I visited the place where I had kept my books and papers. I had fondly imagined that they would be all right there until after the war, but I found the place burned to the ground and the charred remains of my books. I recognised the tin trunk in which I had kept my papers. It was the work of fifth columnists evidently.

I went to the Globe Welding Works and found my car with one wheel off and some vital parts missing. Vertannes said that he would bring the car up and get the parts for it. I agreed to let him have half the sale price of the car if he succeeded in disposing of it and he richly deserves it if he does. I wonder if he will make the effort as he is a very rich man and money means little to him now.

After that I visited the house in Aungbale and found it completely deserted. Robert's motor bike was there and also Harry's car with the dynamo gone. I told Vertannes to take Robert's bike and sell it for him. I found my books and papers still in the house and it was a wrench parting with them. I selected a few books that I thought I could retain until the end. There was also a big box of clothes, evening dress etc which I shall have to leave. In Robert's room I found a pair of grey flannels and some odds and ends of clothing, and his big *sola topee*. I also found two big account books of the Indian firm whose fire loss he was assessing. The whole thing gave me a wrench – these personal belongings have a voice of their own.

Monday, 13 April, Maymyo

I arrived back in Maymyo last night. There was an air alarm at about 10.30 and a second one just a few minutes after the first was over. I went out in the jeep with Bea and Lester to the funk hole in the jungles.

I learnt that Vertannes had brought up my Chev and also Robert's bike. A wonderfully active fellow. One of my main fears now is that my jeep will be taken away by the military. Coming back after the air raid alarm from the jungles, the car was stopped by two sentries on the Mandalay road, but they let me pass when they saw the Chinese government label on the windscreen.

Lester had a telegram from Issie that she had arrived safely in Calcutta. Good news, but the news from the front is not so good. The Japs are at Taungdwingyi. I must hurry up and go as at this rate they will be in Mandalay within ten days.

Wednesday, 15 April, Maymyo

I have just learned that my leave is cancelled and that I have to go to the Front with the Chinese Army as a Civil Liaison Officer to see that the military don't execute Burmese after too summary a trial. I went to the top and saw the Premier, Sir

Paw Tun, who agreed to cancel the order, so I then managed to get my leave permit and also got a permit from the Defence Department. I can't linger here now or else the government will change its mind again and I will find myself at the Front in some impossible anomalous position.

I said goodbye to Swithenbank, who is off with others to Myitkyina for evacuation by air. I have decided to leave the day after tomorrow.

Friday, 17 April, Maymyo . . . Shewbo

I met Bobby while I was on my way to see Vertannes. His orderly spotted me as I was passing in the jeep. It was such a relief to see him. He had just come back from Yenangyaung, which had been demolished. At one time he was surrounded by a ring of fire. I can just imagine the sight. Bobby had passed through Mandalay and found that our house at Aungbale had been burned down.

I have arranged for Bobby to dispose of my Chev if possible, though I doubt whether anything can be done with it at this late stage. Everyone is very jittery. At any time now the Ava Bridge, our lifeline out of Mandalay, may be bombed. There is news that there are a hundred planes at Myitkyina to take off evacuees, but I wonder if this is true. My faith in the government is completely shattered.

I left Maymyo at 1 pm. I went in convoy with Colonel Fraser, I in the jeep and Fraser in his Vauxhall 14. At the 20th Mile we had tea with a couple of army men and talked about the Anglo-Indian camp at Wetwun. I wonder if the refugees will ever get through to India. It seems that what the local authorities are doing in each place is to push their charges on to some other locality instead of arranging for a straight evacuation to India.

We didn't stop at Mandalay but went right down the Mandalay-Maymyo Road and out to the Ava Bridge. The fires had reached the southern part of the town and to the right and left of us all was completely devastated. We had no trouble in getting through the Ava Bridge. I'm avoiding officialdom as much as possible as my one fear now is the obstructiveness of our own officials rather than the Japs.

Saturday, 18 April, Shwebo-Monywa . . . en route Kalewa

Fraser and I left for Ye-U at about 10.30 and had breakfast when we got there. After breakfast we set out for Monywa. It was an awful journey; the road is said to be motorable but it is barely so. And I got burned brown in the sun.

At Monywa we visited the Irrawaddy Flotilla Office and found that the government launch *Corsair* was leaving at 6 pm. There was only deck accommodation, but we hurriedly put our stuff on board. I have a great desire to get away now. All we need is an air raid here and for the crews of the boats to run away and it would be impossible to get to Kalewa. It's only a matter of a few days before the balloon goes up for Mandalay, Maymyo and for the rest of Upper Burma.

I spoke to Pha Htaw U for a few moments on the road as he passed in his car. He was very jittery and told me he was going to do a bolt. I advised him not to go without leave.

We left Monywa on time. What a sense of relief! Fraser has a bottle, or part of one, of good Scotch. I gave myself special dispensation to drink a couple of pegs – the first day this year in which it's been possible to relax. It's a great sense of escape from the enemy, but at the same time I wonder if all the Maymyo folk will succeed in getting away. The rumour that there were a hundred planes waiting at Myitkyina to take off the evacuees appears to have been a false one.

As I was leaving I had a sense of seeing Burma in a new aspect. There was a stretch of river sand, the water lit up by the sunset, a slip of a new moon and a pagoda on a hill.

13

CHRISSIE

March 1986

During my trips to the British Museum in early March, I discovered that the India Office collection held genealogical records. I became distracted from the official files and other records detailing the events that followed the wartime bombing of Rangoon and Mandalay, finding out how to order the birth, baptism and marriage records. I started with my grandfather, Robert, and, after some false starts, tracked back to his father and to my great-great-grandfather, William Stapleton. Putting the information together with records from contemporary travellers and observers, I began to build up a picture.

William set out for Burma in 1819 to trade on his own account with the East India Company. He was bound for Moulmein, at the time not much more than a fishing village on the Andaman Sea, situated at a point where three rivers joined and where the routes lay over the mountains into Thailand. My ancestor must have had a good eye for the main chance, because he was anticipating the advance of the British into Lower Burma; by 1826 the British had set up a military garrison in the town and Moulmein had begun to thrive.

Over the next forty years, merchants – British, Indian, Armenian, Chinese, traders from all round the world – flocked to Moulmein, felling teak from the thick forests around the town and developing timber mills and shipbuilding. I found travel accounts and a book with prints that showed Moulmein as a beautiful town, the colonial buildings covered with stucco-work, and the mosques with their arches and domes. The town was set in romantic scenery, surrounded by small mountains, their summits covered by pagodas and, above the town itself, the old Moulmein pagoda.

William Stapleton described himself as a master seaman. I felt as if I were putting together a jigsaw, with important pieces missing.

It looked as if he was trading along the coast to the Malay peninsula in the years following his arrival. The records showed that his first children were born in Penang, which was then the Prince of Wales Island, my great-great-grandmother simply recorded as 'Mastini' – a Burmese name. By 1838, William was trading regularly with Rangoon in his schooner, the town then barely more than a collection of bamboo huts, and he was registered as one of only a small number of resident British subjects, fourteen years before the British occupied it. Alarmingly, these traders were recorded as 'turbulent' types, more often than not engaged in smuggling silver and gold. However, as the town grew, the family established itself at Monkey Point, a tapering piece of land at the south-eastern tip of Rangoon near what became the docks, where William's son, John, became a seaman like his father and also a prosperous and respected merchant. I found a photograph in a 1910 volume of my grandfather, the young Robert, with an impressive looking moustache and *sola topee*, standing together with his brother in their boat-building yard.

*

I took my father the skeleton of our emerging family tree, drawn on large sheets of paper. We laid it out on the dining table – William's eleven children with three different women, as far as I could track, his son John's children, my great-aunt Louisa and grandfather Robert among the eldest of the siblings; then there were the branches that led off and question marks where the female line should have been.

'I didn't know that Robert was building boats,' I said, giving Bobby a photocopy of the photo of his father, standing proudly with arms akimbo in his boatyard.

'Daddy was doing all sorts of things when he was in Bassein, and of course this was earlier, in Monkey Point. We had a lot of land there. He was trading all along the coast up towards India, you know. Rice . . . teak . . . all sorts – even furniture, sending it off to Europe as well. It was only later on that he settled in Kokine with Aunt Louisa and my cousins.'

It was the women who remained unclear and it was frustrating me. I didn't quite know how to raise it with my father; I felt uneasy, sensing the taboos. Robert's mother's name was Maria, the daughter of another Moulmein trader, married to John Stapleton when she was eighteen, already with two children with John and another one on the way.

'Aunt Louisa had a photo of her which she kept in her room,' my father said. 'She was beautiful and so young, they said, that she would play with the children's toys.'

And my father's grandfather – his mother's father – the Italian, also had his children with a woman called Maria, but I could find no marriage record, nor any clue to her background.

'All the women in the family were gifted . . . artistic, you know,' my father said.

I pushed him a little. 'Didn't you ever talk about who these women were, your grandmothers and their mothers?' I asked.

'Well, my own mother died when the girls were young. And with Aunt Louisa . . . well, there were a lot of things we didn't talk about. Secrets.'

His voice dropped low, stumbling a little on the words. 'There were scandals. And as children we were kept in the dark. The important thing was to look a certain way, wear the right clothes. And of course, all the children went to the best schools – the boys to St Joseph's in Darjeeling. And Lion, well, he was educated in Paris and then at the bar in London.'

My father looked uncomfortable. There was too much covered up, too many secrets that probably would never be told.

14

LAURA

February and early March 1942

That clear evening on the boundary between Burma and India, there was a quite remarkable stillness about the air as we wandered up the hill after our paddle in the Lockchau. I felt almost disturbed when we unexpectedly came across a small gathering. As we approached, we could hear one voice raised above the others – somewhat staccato sounds that cut sharply into the muffled murmur. I stopped a little distance away, uncertain what it was all about, while Julia walked on; but then she turned round, waved, and came back.

'It's all right,' she said, tucking her arm through mine. 'No one will mind if we join them.'

We got closer and squeezed in between some women to sit down. It was clear that the voice was being raised with some vehemence.

'Being in the convent taught me a few things about life. My father gave them money to keep quiet about who he was. In fact I found out that he was actually paying them really well, which was why I was quite favoured as a pupil. Anyway, when I found out that his money was not just educating me but making sure that no one knew about his so-called wife and child, I walked out of the convent.'

'It's not just the Catholic Church,' someone called out.

'No, you're right,' the woman conceded, then picked up her theme again. 'It's just the same with people in the Church of England. They hold their hands up in horror at illegitimate children, but it doesn't stop them socialising with the fathers.'

The light was going and I could see the owner of the voice only indistinctly. Suddenly she stopped and leant over to talk to a companion. There was silence, then a few low murmurs. Some of the women began to move off. I felt slightly uncomfortable and I didn't really want to hear any more, but at the same time I was curious. The woman started again, pulling something across her shoulders and pushing her hair back with her hand. Julia was craning forward to hear.

'Illegitimacy is actually a standing joke in some quarters.' The tone became harder. 'I'll tell you what it's like in one college. I heard that the padre amuses himself by getting the boys to introduce themselves by the names of their fathers' firms rather than their actual names.'

'Are you serious?' There were more indistinct murmurs, and then I heard her again.

'No, this is really true, and can you imagine what it's doing to the children? I'm telling you, I'm really glad people like that are being pushed out of the country. Who needs them?'

There were a number of voices calling out from the crowd, then just afterwards more women began to get to their feet and it broke up. Looking around, I caught sight of Gracie and Lucy moving towards us. I got up and went over to Gracie as she approached.

'I'm afraid we crashed in at the wrong moment.' I needed to say something, but Gracie looked mildly amused at my discomfort.

'We were listening from over there,' she said. 'You know, the Church is a sore point with us and the evacuation has made us all very bitter.'

I couldn't see that it was the right time to lash out in the way that the woman had done. It was demoralising. Frankly, we were demoralised enough.

'It sounds a bit extreme,' I said, keeping my tone light.

Julia turned away, as if to avoid a response. I had obviously said the wrong thing.

Lucy stood in front of me and her voice was fierce. 'Extreme? Laura, I'm sorry if I sound rude, but you must be joking. The Church out here is a complete swindle. My cousin was attached to a mission hospital and when it came to the evacuation, these so-called God-fearing people deliberately didn't tell the servants or make any arrangements for them. Those servants were fellow Christians; they had actually carried on working because the brothers had promised to see that they were all right if the time came to leave.'

'That's terrible,' I said quietly.

'Lucy's right,' Gracie added. 'I've seen the way some of these types have behaved in the ration queues along the way, as if they had some God-given right.'

'Isn't it same the world over? You're always going to have the good and the bad, aren't you?'

'Maybe,' replied Lucy, 'but we're not really interested in the rest of the world, I'm afraid.'

We lapsed into silence. Then Gracie said that the pregnancy was wiping her out in the evenings and that she needed to go back or she would pass out at our feet. So we started to make our way, helping each other along the path in the dark.

I was worried that I had offended them and touched Gracie's arm.

'I'm so sorry. I don't know what you've been through, of course.'

'Don't worry, Laura. It's all right. I'll explain when we get in.' Gracie was friendly, but still tense.

Vera woke up when we came back and joined the rest of us in the women's cabin. We put our bedding across the bamboo platform that served as a bed and we squashed up together.

Gracie said, 'Shall I tell you my own story? Then I think you might understand our reaction. You may not have guessed but, in many ways, that girl was talking about my own situation. The only thing I inherited from my father is my looks and they've been my curse. Ironic, isn't it? Well at least they were until I married my husband, Tim.'

She stopped for a moment, then carried on, smiling slightly. 'Tim's from Tavoy, and I've known him for years. My aunt and uncle, the Smiths, were from there. Actually, my cousin Bertha is coming out on this route, but I'm not sure whether she's got through yet. Well, her parents brought me up really, so I spent all my holidays in Tavoy. We used to go down to the beaches almost every day, and I met my husband there years before we married.'

'They were childhood sweethearts,' Lucy said.

'Mmm . . . Well, he was my best friend, I suppose. I was a bit of a tomboy. Anyway, Tim was commissioned towards the end of last year and I went to stay with friends in Rangoon and got a job as a typist in my father's firm. I knew my father was working there, but he didn't know who I was and I kept well away from his department.' Gracie paused and took a breath. 'My father had a bad – very bad – reputation in the office for putting himself around with the girls.'

Gracie seemed intent on telling her story. I began to realise how the outburst on the hillside had struck a chord with her. The girls were all listening intently. I sat with my knees pulled up in front, suddenly feeling an overwhelming tiredness.

'Despite everything, about a month later, my father spotted me and, sure enough, he soon found a way of coming into my department, and he kept on asking me stupid little questions about my work. Then one day he came right up to me, put his arm round me and suggested I might like to "keep him company". Absolutely straight to the point; no beating around the bush. I pulled away and told him who I was. His face went really grey – utterly shocked. He couldn't say anything, so I just walked out of the office.' Gracie stopped.

'When was all this? You didn't say anything.' Julia was the one to break the silence.

'About a fortnight before I left Rangoon. I got a message saying that I'd been given an air passage to India – priority passage, with no reasons given. That was my father. And some money had been transferred to me. Obviously my father! Anyway, I gave instructions for the money to be transferred back to the payee and here I am.' Gracie gave a short laugh, almost like a dry cough, and looked up at us.

'Didn't he notice you were expecting?' Vera asked.

'I wasn't really showing then. Anyway, I'm not sure he would have cared!'

Gracie didn't seem to be asking for any sympathy, and I really liked her, but she was clearly taking no prisoners. It was shocking. I was uncertain, unsure how to respond to what I'd just heard. So I said, 'But are you all right? And your baby?'

'Oh, Julia is keeping her eye on me, aren't you?' Gracie looked at Julia, who put her hand on her friend's arm.

'At least we are trekking in very easy stages, and the baby isn't expected for another four months – plenty of time to get to Mussoorie!' Gracie smiled, as if to shake off her story. She became the composed young woman of a few hours earlier, and we all relaxed a little.

*

In the end, the evacuation officers kept us in Tamu for four nights. We all decided that it would be good to join up for the rest of the trek and were glad to have a break before what we knew would be the most arduous part of it. Gracie had a sweet nature and made a real effort to reassure me after her revelations on our first night. Vera and I were both able to get some treatment for our infected bites and sores. It was heavenly to relax and the boys also needed to rest; they, even more than we – as Vera repeatedly told us – were more likely to fall prey to fevers if they were tired. There was plenty of hot and cold water and we were supplied with carbolic soap. But the cabins were cramped, the bamboo platforms desperately uncomfortable, making it impossible to sleep well, and the conditions were insanitary. We had to break into our reserves of rice and tinned meat as the camp didn't provide any food rations, so we were glad in the end to set off.

On the second day we were sitting on the slope just below the camp. Appaswamy had brought up a scruffy little grey terrier from the Indian camp. 'He's all alone,' he said. Appaswamy and the boys were now playing together with the dog, running in circles and falling giggling to the ground.

I turned around to speak to Lucy, but she was sitting up stiffly and intently watching the track below us. Then I saw two figures straggling up: a tall woman in slacks, carrying a pack, walking slowly, followed by an Indian wearing a loosely-tied turban and khaki trousers.

'I think it might be . . . can you see?' Lucy shaded her eyes, trying to see more clearly.

'It's my cousin Bertha!' Gracie, was almost shouting, tugging on Lucy's arm and struggling to her feet.

'You're right, it's Bertha, and she's got Kureeya with her. Wait, Gracie. I'm going down there.' Lucy slipped down the slope on loose stones, achieving the final few yards on her bottom, clutching at the ground with her hands. Julia set off more carefully.

Vera and I stayed with Gracie, watching the others rush down the hill. Lucy reached the pair and the two women held on to each other and talked excitedly. Lucy pointed in our direction and we waved back.

Gracie went towards them as the little procession started uphill again.

'Be careful!' I called after her, as she stumbled on an exposed tree root.

As they came up to us, Gracie threw herself on her cousin. 'You look exhausted, but you're here. Please, please, you must tell us about everything quickly. Have you heard from Tim?'

She was right. Bertha looked as if she had reached her limit. Her dark slacks were dirty and frayed around the bottoms, her bronze-coloured shirt hung limply in deep wrinkles, and the brim of her *sola topee* was stained with large brown patches, bulging where the pith had been soaked. Bertha's face looked drawn, but there was something that still indicated a society woman.

'Darling,' she said wearily and still breathless, pulling away from Gracie a little. 'Tim is fine as far as we know. Don't worry. But we didn't have any news of the regiment before we left. How are you?'

'Mother and child both doing well.' Gracie stood back showing off her rounded belly. Then she turned to the man. 'What are you doing here, Kureeya? How is Dick-Baba?'

The Indian turned away, for an answer pulling up the side of his shirt and covering his face with it.

'We don't know, dear,' Bertha said, softly.

'How? Why?' Gracie clung to Bertha's arm. For a moment I thought Bertha would lose her composure. We pressed her to sit down for a while and Kureeya walked away and then stood, motionless, staring out at the hillside that he'd just walked up. Then he squatted down on his haunches, his arms wrapped loosely around his knees.

'I will tell you about it later.' She smiled wanly at us all. We sat in silence, Gracie with her arm round Bertha's neck. Tommy and Ben had squeezed in between us, sensing the mood.

I was the one to break the silence. 'Shall we all get back to the camp so that you can both have some rest. Where are your things?'

'In Monywa!' Bertha smiled wryly. 'This is my exclusive wardrobe.' She gestured down at her clothes. 'I'll tell you about it all later on,' she repeated, patting Gracie's hand and smiling at Lucy.

*

Bertha told us her story later that day. She was now kitted out from our various meagre items of clothing, and was looking fresh and less tired. We were sharing our cabin with other women and children, so we tucked Tommy and Ben in for the night, leaving Appaswami and Kureeya on guard outside. We sat close to each other in the fading light where we could get some fresh air away from the fetid smells of the camp, but still within sight of it.

'I came up to Mandalay at the beginning of January. We knew Tavoy wasn't safe, but Dick had to stay, of course. He couldn't get leave. And the administration could not accept that the Japanese troops would actually cross the border. Anyway, Kureeya was wonderful and asked around until he found me in Mandalay. It was a miracle, really. And then he told me the news about Dick.'

Bertha stopped for a moment. Gracie leant over and rubbed her cousin's arm gently, but none of us said anything.

'I hadn't had any news for weeks, but we all knew that letters weren't getting through, so I thought . . .' She stopped abruptly, holding a bandaged hand across her mouth and looking away briefly. Then she started again. 'But all that time it seems that he had been captured in Tavoy back in January. Kureeya wouldn't stay in the house and then fortunately he managed somehow to get on a train in Pegu.'

'Lucky for him,' I said. 'The trains were packed full when we were leaving for Mandalay.'

'But then we had a terrible time. There was a raid on Mandalay the day after Kureeya tipped up. We were all shocked by that, so we left for Monywa a day or two later.'

'You must have been there a couple of days after us,' Vera said. 'What happened to you?'

'We couldn't get on a steamer. There was a dreadful scrum, so we set out on foot looking for transport. Luckily enough, I had plenty of money with me, so we finally managed to get a canoe. But the villagers were pretty unfriendly and just left us to it. We were rowing for two days, just Kureeya and I, and another man and his wife, so I had to pitch in as well. It was terrifying. You can't really trust the villagers anymore and we were on the lookout for *dacoits* the whole time. I can tell you, we had a pretty narrow escape at one point. There were some shouts coming along the jungle path where it came down to the river and then shots. We just kept going as fast as possible. What else could we do?'

We huddled together as we listened.

'Look at my hands,' Bertha continued, holding them out. 'From the paddles!' We could hardly see them in the dusk, but she told us that her bandaged hand had infected sores; the palm of the other one was scored with rough scabs and her nails were torn and broken.

'Poor you,' murmured Julia.

'Thank heavens, eventually we were picked up by a launch. But the worst thing was when we stopped at night. There were crowds of refugees on the river bank absolutely desperate to get on the boat. Kureeya wanted to get off to make some room for them, but I insisted that I needed him and kept him out of sight of the officials. There were women asking us to take their children, men trying to push the women on board. It was dreadful.' Bertha stopped and covered her face with one hand, rubbing her fingers against her forehead.

'What is being done for them? How can they leave?' Gracie said quietly, after a moment. Bertha cleared her throat.

'One of the men in charge seemed to go berserk,' she said. 'He just added to the confusion by yelling at everyone, waving his revolver around and punching away anyone who tried to get in the boat.'

The others were now just faint shadows in the dark. We sat in silence for a while, each one nursing her own thoughts.

After a while, Gracie spoke. 'Bertha, so wasn't there any news at all from Tim?'

'No, darling. You must try not to worry about him.'

*

On our second day in Tamu we reported to the evacuation office for permits to enter India, only to be told that we had to wait while the numbers of evacuees on the Palel road cleared. We gathered that the narrow, mountainous track was unsuitable for carts or mules and the going was slow. We were finally able to get away on the last day of February after a three-day wait, although we couldn't get a permit for Appaswamy. He had to wait among a crowd of Indian evacuees for further instructions. We left him with the little dog, which had attached itself to him, with assurances that the Family would be expecting him to join them in Calcutta. Bertha had somehow managed to convince the official in charge that she needed Kureeya to accompany her, and we were relieved to have him with us.

We had hired Manipuri porters to take us into the Naga Hills and had reluctantly lost the pony along with the Chins when we arrived in Tamu. We decided to make an early start and were already sorting the luggage with the new porters when the first sounds of the camp waking up gathered momentum. It was going to be a brilliant morning, the hills around already sharply outlined and appearing deceptively close. Within minutes the murmur of voices, punctuated by calls and shouts, was growing louder.

We checked the luggage and that the porters were all ready to start. Vera was standing next to the laden *dhoolies* for what had become her morning routine.

'Are you ready?' Vera barked in fake regimental mode.

'All ready!' we all called back in an attempt at enthusiasm.

'Okay, contact,' shouted both the boys, their daily signal for the start. They were anxious to get going and had been hanging around the porters long before it was time to go.

'Okay, off we go!' Vera called out.

Yes, I thought, but where to, in the end?

*

The boundary with India and our last link with Burma was marked at the summit of a small hill. We all stopped at the pile of masonry that indicated the boundary line and looked back. I glanced at Gracie, who was holding on to the children, one in each hand, visibly upset. I stood beside them, just gazing at the contours of the country we were leaving.

I rubbed the back of Ben's head and said, 'Say goodbye, boys,' and we waved.

I was aware that Vera was moving around rather uncomfortably somewhere near me, waiting for us to move on. Lucy simply stared down at the path that we had just climbed. If her face showed anything, I guessed it was some sort of subdued anger.

Vera spoke up, 'I wish I could say something . . .' Poor Vera, she could never be silent.

Lucy's voice was hard. 'You don't have to say anything. It's not your fault that we've lost our home.' She looked away at the hills again. The porters were trailing up the last bit of the climb. Without the pony, they were struggling with our combined baggage.

Then Gracie said, 'Come on, boys,' and we all moved off.

Julia came behind me and put her arm round my waist. 'It's all right,' she said, 'your friend is no different from many others. She doesn't have any roots in Burma and nothing to lose. It can't mean the same thing, can it?'

We walked in silence for a while, then Julia spoke again, quietly. 'You have to understand that Lucy has gone through hell. She doesn't talk about it now, but her village was attacked by *dacoits*. She saw her village burnt and her whole family was killed because one of the villagers fired off a gun mistakenly – he was just nervous.'

There didn't seem to be anything I could say.

Then she turned to me. 'What about your family?' She carried on before I could answer, 'I know, they probably don't talk about it, do they? But you have to admit to yourself that Burma is your country too, for all your talk about home back in England. It must be the same for you as for us, Laura. It's terrible leaving, isn't it?'

'Yes, of course.'

'Were you brought up in Rangoon?'

'Oh, yes, my grandfather lived in a huge house in Monkey Point, right on the river.'

I thought about the times as children when we used to climb up with him to the glass tower at the top of the house; he would identify all the different ships as they were going past and they would hoot at us – or so we believed.

I smiled at Julia. 'We were very wealthy in those days. The house had a huge ballroom and we would have the most wonderful evening parties . . . Well, that's it. It's all over, I know.'

Julia didn't reply but slipped her arm through mine, and we started down, stumbling and slipping occasionally on small stones that covered the hillside. In front of us, Vera was tagging along behind Gracie and the boys.

*

As we moved into more dense jungle, we became entirely enclosed by giant teak trees, and the branches as they swept down to the undergrowth were covered by thousands of multi-coloured orchids. Everything was quiet except for the penetrating sound of cicadas and the call of birds. After our delay in Tamu it felt as if we had been on the road for a long time; Kokine was a far distant dream. Despite the presence of the others, I sometimes felt incredibly alone. I missed Harry and the dog, our everyday routines and our own wonderful lakes. I couldn't allow myself to think about the men and whether they were still held up in Lower Burma. I was grateful to the children for their chatter, as our own conversation had become hushed and subdued. After our earlier closeness, even Julia and I had sunk back into our own thoughts. We had no option anyway but to move in single file along the narrow jungle path. At the head of the line, one of the Manipuri porters was now leading the way, with suitcases strapped to his back.

Ahead of us, there was a tall, angular man coming down the path, evidently one of the evacuation officers. He was dressed in spotless shorts, a superbly ironed shirt, long khaki socks meticulously turned down and with a handkerchief neatly tucked into his breast pocket. His hair, slightly grey at the temples, was brushed severely back from a low forehead. His shorts almost covered his knees and he had his jungle kit on a leather belt and a revolver in a sheath. But, as the man passed us, what made him instantly remarkable was a gold-rimmed monocle attached to a thick black cord, which he screwed into his eye, examining us briefly, before nodding curtly as he passed.

Julia turned round to me and grinned. 'Now I've seen everything!'

Lucy and Gracie ignored him and walked off up the path with Tommy, followed by Vera and Bertha, dragging a reluctant and protesting Ben.

'Haw!' Julia looked back at me and put an imaginary monocle up to her eye, and we burst into giggles. 'Actually,' she said, sobering up, 'from what they were saying in Tamu, I think that man is supposed to be really awful, the worst official around the camps. If you ask me, he looks even worse than his reputation.'

I agreed. 'We were lucky he was out of the office when we got our permits.'

I turned round and watched his retreating figure, then adjusted my terai hat firmly on my own head and set out again after the others.

*

When we caught up with them, Vera was trying to make conversation with Lucy and Bertha, all the while clutching at wayside branches to help her up the hill. The appearance of the official had lightened the heaviness of the mood we had shared since crossing the boundary into India.

'You don't seem to be winded, Lucy,' I said, gasping for breath.

Lucy shook her head. 'No, I've probably had more practice than you all. I come from a village where the transport is either your feet or bullock carts. I've always preferred my feet.'

'I've got a feeling it's going to be hot very soon.' Julia was pulling off a light sweater. The sky was a blinding blue and without a single cloud.

'Why don't we stop here a bit?' I suggested. 'Look what we've got ahead of us.'

I pointed down. From the top of the hill we could see a tiny thread of road unrolling down into the depths of the long valley below and straggling up another hill. Deep in the valley, rain fell softly while, above, the warm sun had pushed through the clouds and now blazed down on us through the overhanging branches. For a moment, a hint of rain sprayed on us lightly, swept over the crest by gentle winds. Telegraph wires marked the line of our route and the continuous humming provided a bizarre orchestration to the rustling of the leaves overhead and the occasional bird call.

'Phew, the top at last.' Gracie sat down on the short grass and then lay flat. 'I'd better go slowly for the baby's sake. I don't want him turning into a mountain goat.'

The ground was carpeted with tiny star-shaped flowers and there was a strong smell of earth and wild blossoms. One by one we all threw ourselves, exhausted, to the ground.

*

Out of a timeless place, as if from a distance, I heard Vera shouting. Sitting up, I could see that she was remonstrating with the boys, who were squatting in front of a little shrine in the hollow of a large split tree, cleaning it out with twigs and carefully laying little bundles of flowers. I jumped up to see what was happening, shaking my head a little to wake myself up.

'Come away from there, boys!' Vera's voice was louder.

'It's for the god,' Tommy shouted back.

'Come away!'

'I want to be the god,' Ben said and stepped solemnly into the shrine.

'Ben, that's bad.' Tommy turned round, shocked and looking for our reaction.

Vera rushed forward and dragged Ben away from the shrine. Tommy just stood there with a bundle of twigs in his arms.

'They're missing Appaswamy,' I said. I ruffled Tommy's hair and took him by the hand over towards the edge of the cliff. The mists rolled up the hills like soft shaving foam, the dark green slopes dazzling above them in the sun.

*

The next morning Lucy sounded impatient, and she frowned as Vera rearranged the bundles for a second or third time. She had looked disturbed since the night Gracie told us her story. Julia told me about how hard Lucy found it to accept leaving Burma. At the same time, I couldn't say why, but I felt that perhaps she regretted joining up with Vera and me. Ben must have sensed her mood. She was gentle with the boys and, in Tamu, Ben particularly had taken to following her around the camp, his hand pressed against the small of her back. But on the morning we left Tamu, both boys had attached themselves

185

to Gracie instead and they were unusually quiet as they picked up the dispirited atmosphere that seemed to hang around us all.

'Come on, let's go!' Lucy's face was set hard and her hands dug deep into the pockets of her dress.

As we set out, it was difficult to lift the low mood, and I walked silently next to her. We were an odd-looking bunch, I thought, with our creased dresses and trousers, our socks and heavy walking shoes. Vera's feet and ankles still had weeping sores despite our rest in Tamu, and she'd cut holes in her brogues so that she could wear them again. The sole had loosened on one of my own shoes, so I had wound some string around it, hoping that it would hold it firm. There was hardly a wave left in my hair and my face was covered in insect bites. I pulled the brim of my hat firmly down.

Ahead of us we had a short climb to the top of a ridge, and then it was a long descent into the valley. We marched along the ridge in silence, all of us awed by the grandeur of the country, and even the boys were quiet, listening to the bird notes rise from deep in the valleys. As the sun climbed higher, its beam touched the bracken and grass, and streamed at us through the jungle, which rose to meet us like a green wall.

Towards the end of the morning we were walking through a tunnel of tall trees with fantastically twisted creepers rooted into the ground, the path shaded and crowded by a mass of wild flowers and orchids. As it became hotter, the scent of the jungle blossoms was quite overwhelming and I thought of Lion and Robert, wondering if they would be coming through soon and thinking how they would revel in the forest route. I wished they were with us to name the birds and tell us about the plant life. The track had become unusually flat and wide, ferns and shrubs lining the path, and the boys raced along, weaving from side to side, their arms wide. Gracie sang; her voice was surprisingly deep, but clear, and soon we joined her, our chorus echoing back to us through the jungle. Then suddenly the forest with its sunflecked path and gnarled trees broke into open hills again.

After our noon stop, we were walking through a beautiful glen not far from the camp at Lochchau when we came across an old man, looking shrunken and hollow-eyed, under a rough awning made of a *dhoti* supported on four branches. He was thin and lay on his side, his legs drawn up, one arm barely cushioning his head and the other resting loosely over his emaciated hip. He stared out without blinking as we drew near. His face was covered with a film of sweat and his breathing was coming in shallow rasps. There was a swarm of flies buzzing around him.

'Look at his food,' I said, motioning towards the plate of untouched rice next to him, covered in swarming insects.

Vera steered the boys in front of her, catching my shoulder. 'Laura, don't. We can't risk passing on something to the boys, or to Gracie in her condition.'

I hesitated, feeling that moral certainties were becoming unclear. Then Julia came up and stopped by him, and the rest of us hung back with her. Vera came to a halt some fifty yards ahead of us, grasping the children to her.

'He looks almost beyond help, doesn't he?' I said. 'We should at least make sure we tell them as soon as we get to camp so that they can bring him in.'

We didn't have any water rations left but Lucy took over some of the last of the made-up Klim milk we were carrying with us. We propped the old man up and he tried to hold the cup, but his hands were quivering and the contents slopped over the sides. He slowly swallowed some liquid and then turned his face away from us, speaking in a feeble monotone. He said he'd been lying there for two days or so, unable to eat, afraid that he would never get up again.

'Can't we do something about him?' Gracie asked. 'If we could get him to the camp, he could rest there. One of the *dhoolies* perhaps?'

'Memsahib, I will take him. He is very light,' Kureeya broke in. He got down on the ground and eased the old man onto his back and then moved forward in a strange half-crouch, the old man balanced on him like a goblin.

We could smell the next camp well before we arrived. Although we had all been inoculated, we were wary of the sickness that hung almost palpably around the camps, particularly cholera and smallpox. The conditions in the huts and tents were mostly filthy and insanitary and, we were sure, the breeding ground for the chronic diarrhoea that most of us were suffering. The camps just couldn't cope. The medical personnel were already overrun and had no idea how they would manage as the number of evacuees increased day by day.

We decided to send an advance party to investigate the camp ahead at Lockchau. Bertha and Julia nominated themselves and went on with Kureeya and the old man. As the little group left us, the old man muttered feeble farewells. They soon came back without their charge, having left him with the medical team. But they had found the camp filthy, with no night sweepers in operation and the sanitation in chaos, so we decided to continue straight on.

15

LAURA

March 1942

After leaving Lockchau, we slept that night in the open with the men on guard. When I woke the following morning, my back was excruciatingly painful and the muscles in my legs were stiff and cramped. The furious noise of the cicadas and the biting insects had kept me awake, and I felt very little refreshed. The boys were still asleep under blankets, but Vera was sitting with her arms wrapped round her knees, her face almost buried.

She turned her head to look at me and grimaced. 'Laura, I don't feel as if I can walk another mile and we've hardly started.'

I crawled over to her and rubbed her back. 'I know,' I said. 'I would gladly kill someone right now for a cup of hot tea.'

In fact, I had a longing for some fruit – the papaya and mangosteen I loved so much in the mornings. Kureeya had taken over the role of cook since we lost Appaswamy and when the boys woke we ate some rations of rice porridge together and moved off, feeling a little stronger.

It was our eleventh day since leaving Sittaung and it was nearly three weeks since I had left Rangoon. We were all badly bitten by mosquitoes and jungle insects and were suffering from itchy sores and blisters. At the end of every day we fell into the camps relieved, but exhausted and ravenous. We looked forward to the small rations of safe water they gave us in the camps and had learnt to measure it out with care during the day. We were told not to trust the freshwater streams, which were contaminated with human waste and even rotting bodies. As we set out from our site near Lockchau we had only about one cup of clean water left between us for the day ahead.

The trek had now become serious mountain walking. It was going to be a gruelling uphill trek, with the mountains rising to some five thousand feet before going down to Palel.

'Say goodbye to the valley, boys. We need our climbing legs again.'

Gracie sounded cheerful, but I thought it was probably bravado more than anything. It couldn't be easy for her. I felt tired and a little down, and I certainly wasn't ready for the long haul we had in front of us. 'It's the grand march now,' Julia had said to me earlier. 'Let's try and all keep our spirits up.'

I was glad to have the other women with us. We each had our low moments, but would rally round each other. On the whole, the women seemed set on a steely but cheerful resolve and it was difficult to be too gloomy with them. Julia in particular was a steady, optimistic presence. In Tamu she had told me about her experience of the horror of the Christmas bombings in Rangoon, the bodies piled up in the hospital corridors and everywhere the blood, and the weariness as one dreadful day replaced another. She and I had still not spoken openly about our previous encounter, but we often walked together and I felt a tacit connection between us.

*

As the sun rose higher in the sky, we zigzagged our way round cliffs, the scenery once more ruthless and grand. Towering mountain spurs on one side dropped to sheer nothingness on the other.

Since Tamu the stream of trekkers had become more dispersed. We could travel for an hour or more without passing other people, although they were often in view as we rounded a bend or emerged from dense growth. Sometimes we came across a small family group, or an older couple, sitting or lying exhausted at the side of the track. We became hardened, fixed on our own march, trying to keep the biting insects away and blank out the pain in our legs and feet, rarely exchanging more than a cursory greeting.

Suddenly that morning we came across a body. At first we saw a multi-coloured, shimmering canopy of butterflies.

'It's so early for butterflies. Look how lovely,' Vera called out to the boys as we approached. Then the butterflies lifted off, as a single fluttering cloud, revealing a rotting corpse underneath.

We rushed past, pulling the children with us. We made reassuring noises but the sight had chilled us and Vera soon bundled the boys back into their *dhoolies*. We walked on in an uncomfortable silence, every step an intolerable effort.

It took some time to restore calm and our nerves were still edgy when, later on, we turned a corner and came upon two newly heaped mounds. They were evidently rough and ready, shallow graves of trekkers who had succumbed, perhaps through cholera or dysentery and dehydration; so many were ill or suffering from lack of food when they started out on the track, sometimes having spent weeks in camps on the roads from Rangoon or Mandalay. The older people were particularly vulnerable and often ill-equipped for the march.

The boys were now out of the *dhoolies* and running ahead with Kureeya, but Vera suddenly sat down to one side of the mounds and started to cry, taking deep gulps of air. I got down beside her, putting my arm round her shoulders. She was trembling and I could feel her back hot and damp. The track ahead was deserted apart from the boys darting about. Behind us the porters trailed with the baggage and their voices formed a sort of screen, almost a door shutting off our life in Burma. It was a beautiful day, the sky a perfect porcelain blue and white.

I gave Vera a handkerchief and she wiped her face and blew her nose, apologising. We scrambled over to a small ledge and sat staring at the stunning country around us as the porters passed by with the empty *dhoolies* and the luggage.

'You know, Laura, sometimes I have the feeling that this is just a dream.' Vera was unusually still as she looked straight ahead. 'We've got so much beauty around us and somehow that's wonderful, but then the whole thing is a nightmare – an unbelievable nightmare . . . When I wake up in the morning I have a feeling of dread. Maybe I'll never see my husband again. Then we have to get going, put our best foot forward and pretend it's all normal. But we have no idea if the men will be able to get out.' Vera's voice was still shaky.

She turned to me. 'Laura, do you think the boys will ever see Peter again?' I rubbed her back for a while and she tilted her head back, with her eyes closed.

I felt the warmth from the sun powering through my body and suddenly felt very alive. 'Come up in your own time, Vera. I'll go ahead with the others and we'll wait for you further on.'

Vera soon caught up with us. Tommy and Ben were throwing themselves about on the ground.

'We're dying,' Tommy explained, 'and when we're dead all the beautifuller butterflies will cover us like we were the babes in the wood.'

'Stop it, you two!' Vera sounded weary.

'You should let them get it out of their system,' I said. 'It's probably better for them than just brooding over it. They'll soon get tired of the game.'

Gracie and Lucy tried to distract them and soon the death rattles ended. And so we marched, weary animals, two by two, into the camp at Khogkou.

*

There were delays in preparing the evening rice, so we walked onto the hillside outside the camp, leaving Kureeya to guard the boys, who had eaten and were sleeping soundly. The air was cold, but the night sky was clear and the constellations bright. We pulled our coats and blankets close.

I couldn't stop looking at the sky.

'What do they say about drawing down the moon? That's what it's like now – it's so close,' I said. 'We just need a long enough pole.'

There was something magical about the night. We were so high up on the surface of the earth and there was a deep stillness, broken only by the incessant vibrations of the cicadas. We wandered on slowly, occasionally exchanging stories about our families. Mostly, we each sank into our own thoughts.

Then Bertha said, 'The nights, especially moonlit nights like this . . .' She suddenly stopped and said sharply, 'Hang on, that's not the moon.' She was looking over towards the camp.

'It's a fire! There's a fire in the camp!' I sprang up.

'My boys!' Vera screamed, and we all rushed towards the camp.

As we got closer we could see agitated figures darting about, silhouetted against the red glow, carrying buckets of water. The fire was fierce, the flames licking up into the night. We couldn't get close enough to the camp to see it properly, but there were some evacuees milling around and we caught hold of them, asking whether people had been pulled out from the huts. Vera was running to and fro almost hysterically, asking anyone she could where the children had been put.

Gracie and I ran round to the side, trying to reach the camp from another approach and then, as we got closer we could see that, although the fire looked terrifying from a distance, it was in fact some way from the cabins. It was the mat kitchens that were blazing. Julia reached the boys first. Kureeya had left them safely with another family in the cabin when he had rushed out to help fight the blaze. When Vera threw herself through the door behind us, Tommy started jumping up and down, asking if they could go and see the fire.

Lucy had found her way into the cabin by now and pleaded with Vera, 'Oh, let them come. It's all perfectly safe and they're much too excited to stay in.'

'O-ooh, look, look everyone,' shouted Tommy, once outside, hopping around on one foot.

The roof of the kitchen had fallen in, scattering millions of sparks and cinders skywards. The bamboo structure, still glowing and burning bright, remained in place – flimsy, red-hot rods jutting out in the darkness. Then the fire suddenly caught a clump of green bamboo, lighting up the firefighters. Men with green branches and hastily constructed fire beaters were slashing at the flames. Others were chopping out fire circles and throwing buckets of water onto the centre of the fire, causing whirlwinds of steam and ash to leap skywards. The flames hissed, but gradually died down, and spirals of white smoke curled into the darkening sky.

Bertha had been looking for Kureeya and they now joined us, emerging from the dark edges surrounding the dying blaze. Kureeya had been helping to beat the fire and, even in the darkness, by the faint light from the spirit lamps I could see that he was exhausted, his clothes wet with perspiration and clinging to him; he brushed the sweat from his face with the short sleeve on his upper arm.

'What more could we want.' Gracie said. 'Fireworks!'

*

We left Khogkou the next morning in low spirits. The night before, after the fire, we had lost any chance of dinner and we were feeling hungry and tired. I vomited when I woke up and by the time we set out I was still feeling weak. Despite our rest at Tamu, we were beginning to tire earlier each day and Vera was limping badly. But, by a miracle, we were well enough. And, as we moved off and headed towards Tengnoupal up a narrow track, our mood lightened. We were among hills rising on either side, each range a deeper blue, until they seemed to bleed into the distant sky. Soft mists swept up the ridge and, in the east, dawn was breaking as if at the edge of the world. That day's climb was in some ways quite heavenly, despite our exhaustion and stress. We went slowly for Gracie's sake and so that the children could walk from time to time.

By mid-morning the air was clear and cool. Cumulus clouds hung low over the outline of a heavily-covered spur and a myriad of birds flew from the mountain tops to the wooded valley below. It was just such a day that Harry and I used to take a picnic up into the hills above Kalaw when we retreated from the summer heat in Rangoon. The servants would pack up salads and slices of chicken, and champagne to celebrate the holidays. I used to take my sketch pad with me and try to capture the shape of the jungle creeping across the hillsides, and the *htis* of the pagodas glistening on rocky outcrops.

We climbed solidly for two hours, following the line of the telegraph poles as our path zigzagged upwards. Then, from the top of a ridge we could see the ranges beyond.

'I know where that bird's nest is,' Vera said, pointing to a speck disappearing deep into the valley. 'I've been watching it all the way down. It flew from an old tree way up on that hill.' After a pause she said, 'Do you know, in some strange way, I wouldn't mind having another day here; it's so lovely.'

We were resting on a slope to the side of the track after our mid-morning stop, still hungry after our small portions of rice porridge and exhausted from the climb. The boys were asleep in the *dhoolies* and Vera seemed less nervous than I'd seen her since we'd left. Like mine, her hair had lost its wave completely, and she had pinned it tight behind her ears. Since we had stopped in Tamu, and perhaps with some reassurance after crossing into India, she was developing a precarious confidence, her tears of the previous day seeming more a release than a breakdown. Her manner was different from the false brightness she had when we left Mandalay. She was less edgy, her voice softer.

*

Julia fell in step with me. 'It's a beautiful day, isn't it?' Then she said, 'Are you okay, Laura? Do you know, after all this hell, everything might just turn out better than we can even imagine now.'

I smiled at her, feeling grateful that she was there. Since we left Tamu she'd told me something about her life in Rangoon. She still hadn't mentioned Eloise but sometimes, when she looked at me, I felt a strong need to say something.

She came from an old Anglo-Indian family, she said. Her father had a senior job in the port in Rangoon and was regarded as an essential worker, and as such wasn't permitted to evacuate. Her parents were still in Rangoon when she left, but they would join her sister, who had married a junior manager in the oil refinery in Yenangyaung, if Rangoon were to be finally evacuated.

We came to a crossroads, with one track swooping down to the left before it disappeared around a hill and the other skirting another hill on which a group of huts – a small village – was clinging. Most of the huts were quite large with overhanging gables, sporting elaborate and colourful decorations on the front. Many had a pair of carved wooden horns fixed to the front gable.

'This must be Savom, the Naga village we were told about,' said Bertha, joining us. 'They were saying that it has its own qualified Naga doctor and a small hospital, and it's really quite a modern village.' We could hear the sounds of chickens and on the side of the hill there appeared to be a small farm with ducks.

'I'm going to see if I can make myself understood and get some eggs if possible.' Bertha started clambering up the hill. At the same time, a young man, clean-shaven, was walking down towards us.

'Can I help?' He was dressed in khaki shorts and shirt, but was barefooted.

'I'm sorry.' Bertha looked confused. 'I thought this was a Naga village and I was going to look around to see if we could get some eggs.'

'It *is* a Naga village, and sure we can get you some eggs.' The man spoke good English with a noticeable American accent. We all followed him up the hill and then stopped outside a bamboo-and-thatch hut while he went inside. He soon came back out with some eggs in a basket woven of leaves and twigs, and held them out to Bertha.

A group of little children, their heads shaven at the sides, leaving their hair like tight glossy caps on their heads, crept forward and stood around us. Two young girls clung together, giggling.

Bertha took the eggs from the young man, who was holding the basket and looking slightly amused. 'Thank you very much. We are really grateful for them – we've not had any eggs since we started out. The children will be very happy. Please let me know how much we owe you for them.'

'Nothing,' the young man said. 'It's our privilege. Please take them, and we have some fruit also.' A little child was staggering towards us with an enormous basket. 'For the ladies and children.' He bowed simply towards us.

The rest of our group were joining us. Kureeya had the two boys on either side of him, and behind them the others were looking to see why we'd stopped. Bertha held up the basket of fruit and turned back to the Naga to thank him again, but then Vera and the boys ran up and there was much peering in the basket, peeling of bananas, and a chorus of thanks. Then Kureeya hoisted the basket onto his head and set off to join the porters who were still on the path below.

The gifts from the villagers put us in good spirits. The encounter prompted a discussion about how and why the village seemed so prosperous, and whether they were going to be able to keep up their generosity to all the refugees that were coming behind us, all of which engaged us for a mile or so.

We still had several hours of our trek before we would reach Tengnoupal. As we trooped round a bend, Gracie pointed out a thin brown path winding up a distant hill. 'Look, we've got to cover all that yet before we get there.'

*

As we climbed higher it had become fresh, with damp air pressing in from either side. The sky darkened and suddenly it looked as if it might rain. From the valley we could see grey mists sweeping and billowing up the hillside. In front, Vera called out in her shrill voice to the porters and then bundled the boys into the *dhoolies*. I envied the children as they snuggled into their rugs, but even they looked pinched and cold. It was a stiff climb and, as we scrambled higher, we could see a clearer sky on the top of the hill.

*

'Mummy, I'm thirsty,' Ben whimpered suddenly. The bottles and flasks were empty.

'Ben, you know we don't have any water. Don't think about it.' I could hear the anxiety in Vera's voice.

My own throat felt desperately dry and I began to feel like screaming at Ben as his whine established itself as an almost continual soundtrack to our march.

'I really can't stand this much more; it's getting on my nerves and now I'm beginning to panic as well.' Vera was echoing my own thoughts. Then she added, 'Tommy has gone quiet and I'm worried he's getting a fever.'

She stopped the *dhoolies* and felt his forehead. He was lying quite still. Despite the cold air, his face was flushed beneath the smudges of dirt, with patches of dried skin on his swollen lips. In the other *dhoolie*, Ben was crying with small choking sounds, tossing and fidgeting restlessly. We set off again; where the track was wide enough, Gracie and Lucy walked alongside the boys and began singing choruses and telling them riddles to distract them. I did my best to take Vera's mind off things, but we both shot glances at the children every few minutes.

A young, striking-looking woman called out to us from where she was sitting beside the track, in her arms a baby of no more than four or five months. Her hair was oiled back on her head in soft black waves from a high forehead, part-covered by a transparent gossamer scarf of pink and silver. She had a thin pashmina over her shoulders; underneath she was wearing a knee-length tunic with a pink satin jacket and Turkish-style trousers. They might once have been her best, but they were now torn and dirty, the ankle bands and silver embroidery badly torn and frayed. She had a little girl with her, about four years old and very thin, dressed in a tunic suit with peacock-blue trousers, and serviceable little leather shoes. Sitting apart with some bundles and a shabby leather suitcase was a man in a *dhoti* and dark jacket, hollow-cheeked and with deep-set eyes, whom I took to be a servant.

We stopped to talk to her and said hello to the little girl, and Julia and Gracie fussed over the baby. We soon explained about the pitiful state of the boys, and the woman got up to look into the *dhoolies*. Ben was still tossing his head and moaning from time to time, while Tommy was hardly moving at all. She rummaged around in her bundles, then took out a flask and offered it to Vera, pushing it against her arm when she hesitated.

'You must take it . . . for the little boys. We are all right. They gave me extra rations for my two and we are okay. I am feeding the baby. Take.'

The woman had put the baby on her shawl while she looked in the *dhoolies*. I crouched down next to him and carefully pulled back the cloth from his face. He was asleep, his mouth a little open, one tiny hand twitching slightly. I put my fingers over his and then cupped the top of his head. Despite the cold mountain air, it felt warm and slightly damp.

Ben was whimpering again, and I got up and turned back to the *dhoolies*. Vera held him up while he sipped the water. 'Not too much all at once, Ben. You can have some more in a while.' She had to almost force Tommy to drink and she rubbed some water onto his flushed face.

I turned to thank the woman and she introduced herself to me as Jabira Manzoor and her children: Rabia and the baby Jehan. It seemed that her husband ran a dispensary in east Rangoon and the man with the suitcase, Hussein, was his assistant.

We found a wrap in our bundles for the little girl, who looked pinched and cold. We were all so relieved to have the water for the boys that a buzz of conversation broke out.

'I think we'll soon be in Tengnoupal,' Bertha said to the woman. Then to Vera, 'Can we manage both the boys in one of the *dhoolies* for now. That way Rabia and the baby can have the other one.'

The woman was tearful. She started talking rapidly. 'Look at my clothes. They are so foolish.' The delicately embroidered slippers were in shreds; lengths of string had been used to tie pieces of soft bark onto the worn-out toes. 'I thought, since I could take nothing, I should take my best clothes, no? The suitcase has only medicines, tinned milk and some clothes for the children.'

It seemed that her husband had sent them out of Rangoon in January and they had become caught in an evacuation camp in Prome. After the bombing the little girl had become ill and terrified every time a raid started.

She was obviously relieved to talk about what they had been through, and her words came out in an endless stream, punctuated from time to time by heavy sighs. None of us was anxious to start our journey again and she took up the thread of her story. It seemed that after they left Prome they stayed with Hussein's cousin in Mandalay, but the house there was bombed as well. The roof and part of the building had collapsed around them, crushing the cousin's daughter and son-in law under a pile of timber and glass.

She took up the edge of her scarf and wiped her eyes. I looked across at Hussein, who was immobile, his eyes blank.

'So, now at least, there are no more bombs.'

The baby woke up and our new friend arranged her clothes to feed him.

'That poor woman,' Gracie said softly. 'The cousin – what happened to her?'

'She also became very ill – it was too much for her to walk so we had to leave her and come ourselves.'

'How did you join up with the route out?' I asked.

'We had to walk along the river. It was very terrifying, very terrible. We did not think we would live. Every minute I thought *dacoits* would find us or enemy planes would see us. But then a lorry picked us up and took us straight to Tamu.'

'Your husband,' asked Bertha as the woman paused, 'where is he?'

'I do not know. It was his wish only that I should take the children and wait for him in his mother's house.'

'Of course,' said Gracie. 'I'm also going to India to wait for my husband.'

*

A little while after we set off again, I dropped back, needing to be alone for a while. My feet were hurting me badly and I had pulled a tendon above my ankle. I saw Julia glance back and then she stopped and waited for me to join her.

'I saw you with the baby, Laura. He's beautiful, isn't he?'

I was silent for a while. Then I said, 'After Eloise, I lost another one – another baby – nearly five months on. You know, both Harry and I desperately hoped for a family, although we knew our chances were running out. And they had; it turned out that they had.'

'I'm so sorry.' Julia looked up at me and we stopped for a moment.

'Harry was devastated,' I said, 'but somehow we couldn't talk about it. He just retreated from me and then I felt I didn't really know who he was.'

Julia caught hold of my hand. We walked on in silence. I let the memory that had haunted me for so long take me over.

*

I went looking for Harry one afternoon after a lunch engagement. The company had small rest rooms attached to the office in Phayre Street and I thought I could catch him at the end of an afternoon siesta. I had been there before, so I knew my way. I gave a light tap on the door before opening it. The shutters were closed, thin shafts of light thrown across the room and onto the bed. Harry was lying back, propped against a pillow, naked and smoking a cigarette. The woman was sitting on the edge of the bed under the mosquito net. She had long, black hair and small high breasts. I felt as if I had walked into another realm – an alternative reality. I heard a gasp as I stepped back out and shut the door quickly behind me.

Harry and I didn't talk for over a week. He stayed late at the club and we took our meals separately. At some point he said, 'I'm sorry, Laura. Let's just try to get on with things the best we can.' I began to spend more time at the Hut with my cousins and as time went on Harry and I found a different rhythm – a new way to construct our marriage.

*

'Did Harry come to terms with it?' Julia asked. 'Did things get any better for you? I mean between you both.'

'No, it was all awful,' I said. 'Harry was simply awful.'

*

A lone Indian passed us, singing mournfully. His *dhoti* was hitched high on his narrow hips as he strode forward, and the striped sateen of his serge waistcoat clung to his body. He was walking with bare feet, striking a bamboo staff firmly against the earth.

*

Tengnoupal was perched on the highest point of the road. We straggled into the camp cold and almost too exhausted to eat. All four children were wrapped in blankets and asleep in the *dhoolies* when we arrived, and Kureeya and I helped to carry them into the tent before joining the others unpacking the baggage. Afterwards, Vera emerged, pushing the hair back from her face. She had lost weight from her already slim frame and her slacks were hanging loosely from her hips in deep wrinkles. I didn't want to think what I looked like.

She stopped, looked around at the camp and said, 'It's going to be a relief to slip back into normal life again. Back to some sort of civilisation and knowing what's what and who's who.'

I couldn't resist looking across at the others to see the reaction and saw Lucy roll her eyes. Even Gracie let out a sarcastic 'Sure!' Vera reddened, shrugged her shoulders slightly and busied herself with instructions to the porters. That evening we were all too tired to do much more than fall into bed.

It was strange how our mood changed day to day and almost hour to hour. The next morning we made an early start in faint light on a narrow track, to the cries of hornbills flying over the forests. Julia had checked the boys over; they were still listless, but with plenty of water and medicine from the camp dispensary, their fever had abated. Vera felt happy for us to push on and there was an almost palpable feeling of elation that the descent to Palel would be the last part of our journey on foot. While I was packing up I waved my last few emergency biscuits at Bertha and Gracie.

'Look at this! Real luxury. We can picnic on what's left as this is pretty well our last day.'

Mrs Manzoor decided to come with us; with her children and Hussein, we now had four more in our group as we set off.

The sun rose higher and we could make out Palel, some three thousand feet below in the valley. It was a painful walk down the mountainside, every step pulling at our thighs and jarring our ankles, but the sun warmed our backs as we left the high peaks behind us.

As we came closer to Palel, we passed construction sites on either side, indicating the progress of the metalling of the road from Palel, and we passed groups of women picking their way along the path, carrying pans of stones on their heads.

There was a lighter mood across the whole group, a sense that we were almost there. Bertha was walking in front and called out, 'This gets easier!' We had a good rhythm. Both boys had perked up as the morning went on and now scampered by our side. Little Rabia, her body moving gently from side to side with the motion of the *dhoolie*, sat bolt upright and chatted in high bird-like tones to her mother who walked next to her, keeping a protective hand on the baby.

'Fishing rods, Gracie!' Tommy shouted as we passed a clump of bamboo. It was tall and delicate, the pale green rods swaying in the breeze, beautiful leaves at the base of the shoots fluttering and rustling.

We were truly in bamboo country, and bamboo signposts marked the way into Palel. Naga road menders carried water vessels, pans and stone carriers all made from bamboo and, as we passed villagers, we could see that sun shelters, mats, sandals and hats were all woven from it. A group of vividly-dressed Nagas came towards us.

'It's a *tamasha*,' Rabia called out. She was now out of the *dhoolie* and was skipping along the road.

'Carnival time in Palel! How lovely and colourful!' said Vera. She sounded back on familiar ground. I had to admit that it was a relief to feel the pace of life carrying on as normal, even if it were not our own – as if there were no bombings, no war. It was a wonderful scene. The Nagas were wrapped in blankets of blue and white stripes. The women wore rather dashing hats with white pom-poms and what looked like crazy miniature windmills that whirled in a riot of colour, the hat brims sporting multi-coloured streamers and plumes. The young men were decked out with feathers and were carrying alarming-looking guns and spears.

I turned to Tommy and Ben. 'See, boys, how the Naga dancers are wearing hornbill feathers. I'll tell you a story about the Kachins, who live right up near China. During their festivals their leaders wear wonderful headdresses with hornbill and peacock feathers, and also wild boar tusks. The Kachins believe that when people were first created only the children of the sun could dance. One day they invited all the birds in the world to their *manau*.'

'Could the birds dance?' Ben asked, catching hold of my hand.

'Well, they learnt how to dance, Ben, from the children of the sun. On their way back, the birds stopped by a pepul tree because its figs were ripe, and when they stopped they danced the dance they had just learnt. Now, men watching them learnt to dance too, but Hkung-rang, the Hornbill, is said to be honoured because he led the dance. And that's why the leaders of the Kachin dancers have feathers in their hats.' I swung Ben's hand, suddenly feeling hopeful.

'Is that true, Auntie Laura?' Tommy peered round at me, slipped on some loose stones at the side of the road and slithered gracefully onto his bottom.

'Yes, it is. And I'll tell you another story about the Kachins. One of their *nats* is a gnome called Sitnam who lives in the forest and is so clumsy he keeps falling down.'

Tommy started laughing. It was good to have him back on form again.

'Yes, Tommy, you have to laugh when you see him before he laughs first or terrible things happen to you.'

The Nagas were singing as they marched along, but we couldn't get the tune. As they passed I began to sing the Marseillaise to keep the mood going, and then Gracie suddenly shouted, 'Palel!' The top notes of the Marseillaise petered out as we all echoed 'Palel' and moved into gear for the final bit of our trek.

'Civilisation!' Vera tugged at Tommy. 'Look, Tommy, civilisation at last.'

*

Buses, buses and more buses! The boys danced around excitedly.

'Car!' Ben started steering an imaginary motor, making an appalling noise.

'Can we have a tent?' Tommy shouted as we made our way through the crowds and vehicles. 'I want to sleep in a tent tonight, Mummy, can we?'

'I don't know – wait and see. We have to find out where we're going first,' Vera replied, trying to ignore his urgent tugs on her hand.

The place was alive with activity. Lorries and buses screeched their brakes as they steered their way through the crowd, turning and reversing into position while noisy groups of refugees clutching bundles jostled to get into them. It was a one-way traffic jam. We eventually found the camp, which was a collection of little huts and tents, situated in a green bamboo basin surrounded by hills.

Gracie and Lucy were trailing behind us, so we stopped while they caught up. They had decided to go straight on to Imphal rather than put up with the camp conditions in Palel.

'But shouldn't you be taking it easy, Gracie?' I said.

'It won't be that far in the bus and we can rest when we get to Imphal,' Lucy said.

None of the children was in a fit state to go further that day. Tommy had still not fully thrown off his fever, so Vera and

Mrs Manzoor decided to stay overnight and we left our last few biscuits and a tin of powdered milk with them. After some discussion, I said I would go on with the other women and wait for Vera to arrive with the boys the following day. Bertha had been finding the last few days difficult and couldn't face the bus. She decided to wait with Vera, insisting that Kureeya should leave with us.

We paid off the porters, sorted out our bags and pushed our way through the crowds. We left Bertha in the tent, but the boys clamoured to see us off on the bus.

The children clung to Lucy and Gracie, showering them with a mass of kisses. Lucy had often appeared somewhat hard and withdrawn, but she had been immensely patient with them and they adored her in return.

'Will we see you in India? Will you be in Calcutta?' Tommy's face was screwed up, creating a furrow above his nose.

'In Imphal, Imphal, IMPHAL!' Ben jumped up and down.

'Listen, you lot.' Lucy bent down to them. 'Whatever happens, let's make sure that we see each other in Burma, back home. Right?'

'RIGHT!' they shouted.

We all waved and shouted as the bus moved off, leaving Vera, her long cotton dress flapping slightly around her ankles, waving a handkerchief at us until we were lost to view.

16

LION

April and May 1942

Lion got away just in time, avoiding both the retreating army and the worst of the rains. His diary entries show that his frustration and anger blocked out any sadness he might have felt in leaving. He was lucky enough to link up with fellow trekkers who had the influence and money to buy porterage and access to a route which would take them to Imphal on a more circuitous track, avoiding the military on the Tamu road and the evacuation officials who, they considered, were as much of a threat to their safe progress out of Burma as the Japanese. In some ways, Lion was now on familiar ground, however arduous the trek, hiking through the jungle as he had on his more youthful adventures with my grandfather.

Chrissie S.

Monday, 20 April, en route to Kalewa

The journey is getting monotonous, passing all day through dry arid country with sandbanks on one side or another and, on the opposite bank, precipitous sandy cliffs and low ranges of hills in the distance. There are boatloads of refugees painfully making their way upstream, as often as not towing the heavy country boats. They are packed in like sardines so that one wonders how they will survive the awful journey. The *Corsair* is doing about four miles an hour.

We arrived in Kin in the afternoon, where a military man, a captain, got on board. He was on his way to Kalewa, then after reporting there he is due to go to Maymyo. The question is whether Maymyo will still be in British hands by the time he gets down there. I think we have only just got away in time and I have serious misgivings about whether all the women and children from Maymyo will be able to do the same. It seems that there's no through traffic on the Kalewa-Tamu road, only a few military lorries and lorries for the PWD people engaged in making the road. It looks as if we will have to get to Sittaung and make the trek from there to Tamu.

We stopped for the night at Thindaw. The flat boat tied up to us was full of Indian refugees, an orderly, respectable crowd, but they were chatting all night and babies were squealing and crying at all hours. I pity them as there is a difficult time ahead for them.

I gave my full dress trousers to Murthi, who is now the most smartly dressed man on board as he also has my silk shirt.

I had three pegs of Fraser's sixty year-old brandy.

Thursday, 23 April, Kalewa

The country has become more hilly. I must be mentally fatigued as I can't seem to manage to read any poetry. The river is picturesque enough but I can't pay it enough attention. Kalewa is prettily situated but the town itself is filthy and full of smells.

We saw Tin Tut, the evacuation officer and second-in-command. He was very offhand in his manner and received us at the foot of his back steps in a very smelly part of his compound without inviting us in. He suggested that the best thing we could do would be to go to Mawlaik and he gave us a note to the effect that we were permitted to do so. I'd like to know under what law we are prevented from going to Mawlaik anyway if we can find means of getting there.

We installed ourselves in the *Search*, a government launch, and later found that there were ten nurses from the civilian hospital who were travelling by this boat also, as well as 150 wives and families of Indian sepoys. I spent the evening watching them installing themselves on board.

Friday, 24 April, left Kalewa en route for Mawlaik

We left at dawn. It's pleasant country, now fairly wooded with hills rising much higher. At about 1 pm we met the boat *Chindwin* with Sutherland on board. He ordered our boat to stop merely in order to come on board and show his authority to us. A most objectionable fellow. He came up the gangway and, without greeting us in any way, asked if we had any authority to be on board the boat. He said to me, 'Have you any papers?' I asked, 'What papers?' Response: 'Papers giving you authority to be on this boat.' I produced the chit given by Tin Tut. He exclaimed, 'Oh, this is signed by Tin Tut,' as much as to say the authority was not good enough. His manner was most offensive and, when we said that we intended to go on to Sittaung, he at once said that there was no transport going there. Fraser then remarked that in that case we had better move our things at once to his boat and return to Kalewa.

Sutherland said that he'd be back tomorrow and we had to wait for him. What for? We are not pauper evacuees. I mentioned the possibility of going up to Thaungdut. He at once said you can't go there without transport. His meaning was obvious – he had control of the transport and if we wished to go independently of him he was going to withhold all transport facilities from us.

So this is Sutherland! A little man with a short pointed beard. We were wondering what to expect from a remark made by Tin Tut – he said that it would help if we got him in the right mood, which at once made me bristle and ask why members of the public should be victims of the moods of officials. When I told Sutherland that it was one of his own colleagues who advised us to come up and said that we could get transport, he exclaimed that he knew bugger all about it. I could have retorted that there should be greater coordination between evacuation officials. It seems that each of them is so inflated with a sense of his own power that he is not bothering to keep the others informed about the state of affairs within his own jurisdiction. They are acting like independent potentates.

There were heavy monsoon rains in the afternoon. It kept up for several hours. We got into Mawlaik at about 6 pm and I saw Robert at the top of the landing stairs. He didn't see me and after asking who the passengers were he walked away. Acheson came to meet the boat and asked me whether Sutherland had seen our papers; I said yes. He then asked where we were going to be put up and I replied that Sutherland had said the camp. He replied, 'Then you must come to the camp.' At this I flared up and asked him what he meant by saying that we must go to the camp. Were we a couple of convicts? Couldn't we put up with friends if we want to? I then told Acheson that Sutherland was a hectoring, rude, insolent fellow and that neither Colonel Fraser nor I intended to have anything to do with his evacuation arrangements. What right had a man of this type to be in a job in which sympathy and patience are the chief requisites? I can see him intimidating evacuees and making them thoroughly miserable.

We move into the Deputy Commissioner's house tomorrow, but tonight we are sleeping on board.

Saturday, 25 April, Mawlaik

We had an awful night on board. There were women and children squealing and crying, resulting in very little sleep. This morning we moved our things to the DC's house. Robert sent a bullock cart to take our kit. Robert is staying at the *dak* bungalow and it seems that he and I will now be travelling together, as if nothing had happened. There is accommodation both at the *dak* bungalow and the Circuit House, and yet that insolent swine Sutherland wanted us to be put in the camp which is just near the Circuit House – a mat barracks in which one would be ashamed to house coolies in normal times. I am prepared to put up anywhere when circumstances require it, but when there is accommodation available of the kind one is used to and to which one has a right as a government servant, it's insulting to be asked to stay in coolie barracks.

It's arranged that we should go in the government launch to Thaungdut and from there trek across to Imphal. Our party will consist of Fraser, Robert and myself, together with two Sikh traders and a man called Dillon, the brother of one of the local officers. The DC will arrange for transport.

Mawlaik is a most picturesque place. I walked through the main street with Robert and Fraser and bought a pair of rubber shoes. There wasn't any liquor available except six bottles of Spanish red wine in a Chinese shop.

Sunday, 26 April, Mawlaik

Our plans are changed. We are now to go direct from here to Imphal via Shuganu, cutting out Tamu for fear of obstruction by the evacuation authorities there. The evacuation officer at Tamu is reputed to be a much worse bully even than Sutherland. It seems he is a real head case and there have been complaints about him but the government hasn't done anything about it. We are really getting away as much from our own damned officials as from the Japs.

There was heavy rain all day and it was very cold. After breakfast I got into bed and covered up with blankets. We interviewed coolies for the journey and in the afternoon paid five rupees advance for each of forty-nine coolies for transport up to Sunle. From Sunle we will get Manipur coolies. If Stewart hadn't exercised his influence as DC we would have been helpless. He's a splendid fellow and an admirable host.

In the evening the rain stopped. We walked to the *dak* bungalow and then on to Dillon's place where we had French Vermouth. I had a look at the luggage belonging to Dillon and the two Sikhs; they are taking heavy fifty-pound packages, including sewing machines, radios etc. They are managing to get across with most of their stuff. We've been reduced to nix.

I got back to the house dead tired. Stewart produced some Black Label. There is radio news that Mandalay has been bombed again. All telephone and telegraphic communication with Maymyo and Mandalay has been cut off and there is no hope of restoration in the near future. I pray that Bobby and Harry are all right.

Monday, 27 April, Mawlaik

We are going to leave tomorrow early in the morning, so we spent much time arranging transport. The coolies didn't turn up until 7 pm this evening and it was a great relief when they arrived. In the evening Stewart received a telegram to say that he has been granted leave. He has decided to follow us the day after tomorrow as he can catch up by boat. In the evening I had three pegs of Black Label with Stewart to celebrate the good news about his leave being granted.

Tuesday, 28 April, Mawlaik and en route India. First stop Sadwin
We were kept busy in the morning making arrangements for our start. And high time too as the Japanese are at Meiktila and also within a hundred miles of Mandalay from the Taunggyi direction. God help those left behind at Maymyo and higher up. And those lower down in places like Pakkoku and Myingyan. Sutherland didn't visit us.

The baggage was all taken to Dillon's place for allocating to coolies. We are going to have fifty-two coolies making a start from there, with Stewart following up with about six or seven more and his three dogs. We start at 1.20 pm, with our destination Sadwin, nine miles from here, where we will wait for Stewart to arrive before making the next march.

It was a pleasant walk, on the whole through flat, well-wooded country but with hills on either side. We arrived at Sadwin at about 5 pm but some of the coolies didn't get in till a couple of hours later. Robert and young Singh bagged some green pigeons and doves. The Sadwin *dak* bungalow was a dirty little one and much too congested with our crowd. My liberal potations of rum are keeping me going; I wouldn't have survived the journey so far teetotal.

Wednesday, 29 April, Leave Sadwin and stop Myinwun
It was raining in the morning. There was a row between one of the coolies and Robert's bearer. One of the Burmese coolies cut him on his hand with a *dah* and Robert struck the wrong man. I managed to calm them down after some trouble. Stewart arrived late morning and we left for Myinwun. It was a pleasant walk of about nine miles or less along the bank of the Mawku Chaung,

which was a rocky stream – for the most part dry but with deep pools at intervals. We bathed in the stream in the evening.

Thursday, 30 April, Myinwun . . . Dathwechauk

We left about 8 am, passing Yezon, with a filthy little forest rest house there about three miles or so from Myinwun. After Yezon we started climbing once we left the Mawku Chaung behind. Getting round towards the summit of the range, at intervals we caught sight of high mountains to the north and to the west, forming the boundary between Burma and India, and the Chin hills. Magnificent views. We reached Dathwechauk in the afternoon and Fraser, Stewart and I polished off a bottle of Gordon's gin. The rest house is indescribably filthy and had to be cleaned out. For some reason the food boxes arrived late and we didn't have breakfast till past four. At night we were too tired for dinner and cut it out altogether. The gin didn't help.

Friday, 1 May, Dathwechauk to Camp Sunle

We were up at 4.30 this morning and left camp at 6.20. It was a pleasant descent into the Kabaw Valley, the notorious valley responsible for so many deaths by black-water fever. We didn't go to Teinkaya and Htinsin as at first intended as these are on the Tamu road and we were anxious to avoid contact with the military and the evacuation authorities. We were led by the Htinsin headman and his brother by a short cut to Sunle or a spot near Sunle, where we crossed the Tamu road and camped in a hut at the foot of the hills which form the border between Burma and Manipur. Some elephant men had taken possession of the hut and had to be turned out. It was pleasantly situated by a pebbly stream. From our glimpses of the Tamu road it's pretty bad and I should think it's impassable in the rains.

Sunday, 3 May, Sunle to Khengoi

Yesterday we halted at Sunle to wait for the Manipuri coolies and paid off the Burmese lot. I had a pleasant rest, reading the Children's Book of Knowledge belonging to one of the two brothers while young Singh read the Encyclopaedia of Sexual Knowledge. Stewart bought a calf and we fared sumptuously and so did his three alsations.

Today was a most tiresome day's march, with the stiffest climb I've ever had and water was scarce. We left about 10 am and arrived at Khengoi at 6 pm. We had glimpses of the Kabaw Valley from time to time. The road was no more than a footpath which all but disappeared at times.

The Chin coolies all arrived in good time but the Manipur coolies lagged behind and many of them didn't get in till 10 o'clock.

I couldn't sleep as I was too tired. Stewart is very generous with his drinks and produced some Johnny Walker and I had three pegs. At what point we crossed the border into India is not known. Not that I cared either. I've been saying that I would leave Burma without any backward glance or regrets and so it was best that I didn't even know when I actually left the country.

Monday, 4 May, Camped at Khengoi

We were too fatigued to go further today, but we had to stop here anyway as we had left ten packages behind at Sunle and had to send coolies from here to collect them. There were two packages of Robert's and six belonging to the Singhs, one of which contained the queer assortment of books, including the Encyclopaedia of Sexual Knowledge and the Children's Encyclopaedia.

Yesterday there had been a long palaver about needing to discard some of the luggage and Stewart had said that the only solution was for him to stay behind. This frightened the Singhs into releasing some of their useless packages.

Khengoi is an indescribably dirty Chin village. The villagers obviously never bathe. There was no water near the place and we couldn't have a bath of any sort today. The road to the village is closed because of a ten-day feast during which it appears that it is their custom to discourage people from entering the village and no villagers leave the place. This means that we have to make a stop of two days to arrange for transport.

They had a *manau*. There was quite a crowd of unkempt women, children and men. Four men played military calls on bamboo trumpets which were indistinguishable from ordinary military bugle calls. They played a sort of duet with one pair of trumpeters answering another pair, and four drums. There was a large earthenware jar of rice spirit fermenting with a bamboo pipe stuck into the middle of it and it seems that the villagers have pulls at it all day long. Dancing and love-making goes on without restraint, or so Stewart tells me.

The village is full of pigs, but none are for sale; the villagers are very independent.

We are at an altitude of 3,500 ft. and it has kept cool all day. In the morning we heard gibbons or hoolock monkeys crying out in the distance. Yesterday's march was through evergreen forests and Khengoi is situated in the midst of evergreens – very wild country. When we went to the *manau* we displayed our revolvers for fear of treachery on the part of the Chins.

The hut is very basic. We have bamboo leaves for a roof and four of us sleep on a split bamboo platform which covers about half the area of the room, which is about 12 square ft. The hut walls are split bamboo as well and it's just like a Hollywood conception of jungle huts, with the whole atmosphere quite unreal; there is something stagey about the whole business. However, behind all this is a grim reality. My thoughts keep going back to those we left behind in Burma who may never be able to get away at all. We've been without news since 28 April and at the rate the Japanese were moving up I shouldn't be surprised if Mandalay had not fallen by now.

The Chin villagers invited us to the *manau* and we set off in procession from our hut to the village, which is about half a mile away. Stewart was leading in his blue Shan *bawmbies*, I next with my red ones over which I was wearing my Japanese kimono, with my revolver fastened to my waist over it. My dress was completed with a tam o'shanter. Fraser and Robert followed and the Singhs, Dillon and the servants brought up the rear. We proceeded to the village to the tune of a dead march played by two Chin trumpeters who performed on their bamboo trumpets. They had evidently exhausted their repertoire in the morning and the dead march was by way of variation. There was a ceremonial offering of some eggs, two bottles of rice spirit and a white cockerel. Primitive torches and no lamps of any kind. The *manau* consisted of a ring of young men and girls with interlocked arms swaying from side to side to a not unpleasant dirge. In the centre, a young woman was dancing, if bobbing up and down slowly in time to the music can be called dancing. The chanting was quite hypnotic, the dancers all being more or less under the influence of the country spirit which they had been apparently imbibing all day. Two girls were seated with their arms around each other, one of them obviously squiffed. One couple got worked up to the point of kissing each other in public after the dance. The father of the girl immediately sent her away.

At night there was a leopard prowling around our camp and disturbing the alsations. At the *manau* we took the rice spirit offered but I surreptitiously threw all mine away. It was dark enough to do it without detection.

Tuesday, 5 May, Camp Khengoi

We have another day's wait for the baggage from Sunle and we can't start until the Chin coolies return from their own village; they are not due back until this evening. It's very tedious waiting and the lack of water for bathing and washing is a real discomfort. The rain is keeping off although the sky is overcast. I wonder if Mandalay has been taken yet.

Wednesday, 6 May, Khengoi to Mombi

Our intention was to go as far as a place called Yowpi, said to be half way between Khengoi and Mombi. Actually, we carried on right up to Mombi, the first half of the journey being a terribly stiff climb up to about 6,000 ft at a point where the footpath joins the broader bridle path. Here we were in a region of oak and pine, with high mountain ranges to the west and north.

The whole day's march was through evergreen forests. Very picturesque.

The name of our destination – Yowpi – ironically means 'arrived at' in Burmese, but we never seemed to get any nearer to it. And in the end we missed it, as the village lay below our bridle path and we couldn't find any entrance to it. I felt sorry for the headman as he had prepared a hut and a reception with a fanfare of trumpets to welcome us. He followed us to Mombi and instead of getting a reward got ticked off by Stewart instead for not having arranged for someone to wait on the road to show us the way into the village.

We got to Mombi at about 6.30 in the evening – not bad going for such a strenuous march. We had been told there was a good camp which had been put up by the Imphal district office, but on arrival we found it to be a miserable hovel and made up our minds to sleep outside, though I abandoned that idea when I found that it was so cold. I made a camp cot out of a row of *pahs*. Robert slept outside on the veranda and so did Stewart. Fraser had a bed made of the two planks from the front door which we wrenched from its sockets.

Shuganu was supposed to be two marches from Mombi. But we could see it from the heights above Mombi, as well as the ancient Lake of Loktag. We found out that Shuganu was only 15 miles away, so we decided to do it in one march.

Thursday, 7 May, Leave Mombi and arrive at Shuganu

Not far below Mombi we came to a stream, our first sight of anything more than a trickle of water since we left Sunle. It was a pleasant walk which I would have enjoyed more if the long march on the previous day hadn't tired me so much. The view from Mombi of the Shuganu plain was very fine. It was pine and oak all the way till we came down to the level land. Between the 51st and 52nd Mile from Imphal there was a suspension bridge over the stream, which had now become quite sizeable. Again, at about eight miles from Shuganu there was another suspension bridge, a large, well-constructed one with two cables. The first bridge was suspended from a single cable and swayed about dangerously. Some of the planks were missing in the middle and I went over very gingerly, much to the amusement of the two coolie girls who were carrying our baggage with 50 male coolies. We arrived at Shuganu at about 2 pm. The journey after we reached level ground had been extremely tedious owing to fatigue. My feet too were sore and I'm sure I couldn't have done another mile after reaching Shuganu.

Friday, 8 May, Shuganu to Imphal
We arrived after a truly awful bus journey, the 40 miles between Shuganu and Imphal being covered in over three hours. The road was very bad though level-going all the way. At Imphal we failed to get any accommodation at the *dak* bungalow which we were told was reserved for generals and high military officers. After eluding all evacuation officials since we left Burma, we found that we had no option but to go to the evacuation camp.

We had a much desired tea after we got here – bully beef and hard-boiled eggs – also a bath. The camp consists of bamboo huts each large enough to contain about a dozen or more people. The beds are low bamboo structures like platforms.

Our servants were told to stick to their claim to be Portuguese or Anglo-Indians.

From *The Statesman* we learned about the quick march of events in Burma: the fall of Mandalay, Maymyo, Lashio etc. And we also learned from other evacuees in the camp of the bombing of Monywa, Kalewa, Shwebo etc. It was heavy news and I went to bed depressed, thinking about Harry, Bobby and all those who haven't come through yet. It's possible that they are well on their way, but we have been without any information about them ever since we left Mawlaik.

Saturday, 9 May, Imphal to Dimapur
We left Imphal at 5.30 in military lorries. It's lovely country with most impressive scenery, but I was not in a condition to

appreciate it, cooped up as I was in the lorry and sick with the fuggy smells inside. We covered 133 miles between Imphal and Dimapur, changing lorries after Mao, the half-way place, at about 5,700 ft. We had some food out of our tinned provisions and a nap at a delightful inspection bungalow there, above the main road. General Wavell passed while we were at Mao.

We reached Dimapur at about 7 pm and went to the evacuation camp. The camp commandants had a tendency to be somewhat Sutherlandish.

We left camp at 11.30 pm. There was a scramble for accommodation on the evacuation train, preference obviously going to some who were there before us. At the last moment I rushed from the evacuation train to the Assam Express. Stewart was already installed in an intermediate compartment. Most uncomfortable journey; the three alsations were a damned nuisance.

Monday, 11 May, en route to Calcutta on the Assam Express

We arrived at Pandu at about 9.00 yesterday morning and had to wait till night for the Assam Mail. We spent most of the time crossing the Brahmaputra on the ferry instead of waiting at the station, and I was overcome by a feeling of lassitude. There were several wounded officers on board. Before the train started a man called Ballantyne from the telegraph service came in with a mountain of luggage. We were frosty towards him, but relations improved later on; after all, he had every right to insist on getting in.

We got to Calcutta at 6 pm, five hours late. We went to the Grand Hotel as there was no accommodation at the Great Eastern and Robert went to Spence's, near Government House. Stewart, Fraser and I went to the Grand and at once met half of Burma there.

We came across Harry, which was a great relief. There is no news yet of Bobby or of Lester and Bea.

Tuesday, 12 May, Calcutta

Lester and Bea haven't arrived, although Bobby tells us he took them to Myitkyina after they closed the air lifts from Shwebo. There is disconcerting news about the bombing of the aerodrome at Myitkyina and the cutting off in Burma of thousands who have to trek along the terrible route to India through the jungles of the Hukawng Valley. How many will survive the journey?

Harry and I visited Robert and then went to the Tiger cinema after dinner. It was a very silly picture with Tom Walls and Ralph Lynn in *Stormy Weather*. As we left the cinema there was a thunder clap followed by some others. Exactly like an air raid.

17

CHRISSIE

April 1986

Some time in February I started looking for Vera Langham, writing to the Burma Star Association and the Britain-Burma Society, both of which promised to circulate my details and my search through their newsletters and various contacts. In the middle of March I had a brief note from the secretary of one of them, giving me an address in West Sussex. I was excited to know that Vera was still alive and wrote almost immediately. I had a brief note back about a week later.

> 22 March, 1986
>
> Dear Chrissie,
> I was so very sorry to hear that Laura had died. We lost touch many years ago, but we still have such fond memories.
> Why don't you come and have tea with us one day. It is so pretty here in the spring and I will see what I can remember that will help you.
> Yours sincerely,
> Vera Langham

Vera added a phone number and we arranged that I should go down on a Sunday in the middle of April. Her voice sounded young still and, I was surprised to note, had a hint of a Scottish accent. She must be in her mid-seventies, I thought.

I drove down through Crawley, heading for a village near Pulborough, on the edge of the South Downs. I had to stop from time to time to check my map, but the Sussex roads were pretty, with their thick hedgerows, village greens and ivy-clad pubs. I pulled into Vera's front drive around three o'clock, driving on gravel up to the front of an attractive red-brick house, 1920s I thought, excited as I stepped into the porch and rang the bell.

Vera was taller than I expected, and thin, with a heavy cardigan hanging loosely from her shoulders. Her eyes were a pale blue, slightly sunken into her head, her hair waving gently back from her face and held in place with hair slides. She smelt faintly of attar of roses.

Once we were settled in her living room, she had photos to show me: Peter and her in front of their house in Mandalay; Tommy and Ben with their *ayah*; holidays in Kalaw. We had teacakes and shortbread, and Vera had baked a Victoria sponge. She told me about how she had moved to Burma when she really hardly knew anything about anything, but sometimes you just have to take a chance, she said. She had met Peter when he was on leave in Edinburgh and she'd fallen in love, as young girls do.

'I wasn't prepared for Burma,' she said, 'and I suppose in some ways I never got used to it. The heat, the way of life. But, of course, Peter loved it.'

'I gather you're on your own now, Vera,' I said, hesitantly.

'Yes, my husband died nearly twenty years ago. He ended up coming through the jungles – the Hukawng Valley route – during the monsoon. He wouldn't talk about it, but it took him two months or so to get through and I know he suffered very badly, and he was terribly ill with malaria and dysentery when he arrived, and pretty well starving. I was with the boys in Darjeeling at the time, for their schooling, so we didn't see him until he came out of hospital.'

'Did he join you after that?'

'Well, he did, but then he was back in Burma, serving with the Chindits. They needed men who knew the place. So he went back in and we didn't see him again until it was all over.' She stopped for a while.

'He never talked about it. But that's what happened. The terrible deaths they saw – all that suffering and the jungle fighting. Such young men. They all kept it to themselves; it shut them off. And then Peter had health problems for the rest of his life, really . . . But part of it was in his mind. He couldn't forget anything.'

We were quiet for a while after that. Then Vera said that Tommy would be dropping in to join us. Ben, unfortunately, had moved with his family to Canada, where he worked for a large corporation. We chatted politely for a while, drinking light Darjeeling tea, talking about whether I liked teaching and how lucky I was to have such long holidays.

*

When Tommy arrived I was unreasonably shocked to see a stout, middle-aged man, my image of the little boy so strong from Laura's story. He worked for the district council and had something to do with planning.

'Glad to meet you. This is a good thing. I can never get mother to talk about Burma.' He seemed pleasant, shaking my hand warmly.

But Vera's memories of Mandalay were vague, limited to the long days when Peter was away and the tedium of tea parties with the other women, the dreadful heat and dust, which she never got used to, and her terrible fear when the boys were born. Then there was the shock when they had to leave and the strange exhilaration of the trek, despite everything.

'When I think about it now, the country was very beautiful, but it wasn't comfortable like our lovely hills here,' Vera said. 'I still think about those wonderful views we had on the trek. It was as if you were on top of the world and for a while everything else – the war, the lives we had left – just disappeared. I shall never forget it. Did you ever find any of Laura's sketches, Chrissie? She used to take her sketch book and pastels out sometimes.'

'No, I wonder what happened to them.'

'She was very good . . .' She trailed off, then started again. 'But the boys don't really remember anything. You don't, do you, Tom?'

'Well, I do quite a bit, but Ben doesn't really.'

I thought about the boys riding high in their *dhoolies*, the way that they'd helped to draw the women together.

'From what Laura wrote, I think she really appreciated having you boys there,' I said. 'I suppose it gave everyone a focus – you know, distracted them.'

Vera seemed to think about it and Tom smiled at me, perhaps trying to bring back some memory, some image.

'You were so lucky that you didn't get ill,' I said.

'Well, we did. We did get ill.' Vera stopped for a moment, looking at me with her pale eyes, rubbing her lips. 'We all suffered from the food and the conditions, all of us. I think we just lived on tinned meat and dry biscuits practically from Mandalay until we got to Calcutta. The sanitation in the camps was awful, Chrissie. People just fouled the paths because they didn't want to use the facilities in the camps – the conditions were so dirty; they just couldn't cope with all the people. There was rubbish everywhere and there was a lot of cholera after we left Tamu.' Vera fidgeted with her plate. 'We had to put up with mosquitoes – you wouldn't believe – and there were leeches, which even got down the sides of our boots, and flies everywhere. The boys got malaria, and Laura did as well at one point, but we just got on with it. And we had the other women as well, of course. I don't remember their names now, but we were quite a crowd.'

'Tom, do you remember Lucy?' I asked.

'Yes, I think so, vaguely. I remember a dog,' Tom said. 'Did we have a dog with us?'

'For a little while, in the camp in Tamu. Laura wrote about a little dog.'

'Really? I don't remember a dog,' Vera said.

When we'd cleared away the tea things I asked Vera if she'd met Laura again once they got to India.

'Unfortunately,' she said, 'we lost touch while we were there, because I was in Darjeeling and your family ended up in Mussoorie. It was a shame, really.'

'Did you ever meet up again?'

'Yes, we did. We went to a meeting, one of those reunion things in London, and then we met for lunch once. But you know, you end up just getting on with your lives, don't you? That's just what happens. You don't really look back. At least, I didn't.'

18

LAURA

March 1942

The thirty-mile journey north from Palel to Imphal was a bus race in convoy along virgin road still being cut into the hillside. The wooden seats were unbearably hard for our sore and aching bodies, and we all clutched the seat backs in front of us to avoid being tossed into each other's laps. Gracie, across the aisle from me, was trying to sit upright, and looked pale and tired, her lips taut. We had tied scarves and handkerchiefs round our noses and mouths against the dust that swept in through the open windows.

'Gracie, are you all right?' I leaned across the aisle, pulling my scarf away from my mouth and shouting above the noise of the bus and the murmur of voices.

'Well,' Gracie said, with a weak grin and clutching at my knee as we careered round a bend, 'actually I feel terribly sick. I don't know if it's the baby objecting to the bus.'

I pulled my scarf back again and stared out into the paddy fields that lined the dust road. As we manoeuvred round a corner, I looked back and saw the road disappear behind a bend, a line of trucks crawling along a distant ledge and the hills themselves fading into the pale sky.

'I'm feeling homesick already,' Gracie said after a while. 'Maybe it's seeing that little village and the paddy fields.'

Lucy turned round from the seat in front where she and Julia were sitting.

'You know what, I feel like a victim being taken for their last ride!'

'You gloomy things,' I said, leaning forward, 'I'm just glad I'm not in the last bus swallowing all the dust.'

The journey was terrifying, but I tried to keep my mind blank. I thought, It's just this bus ride and then we've made it. We're safe.

Dust was being thrown up in clouds all around us. Our driver was wearing an old woollen hat and only his eyes appeared above the scarf tied firmly over his mouth. There were half-smothered sounds of voices chattering in Hindustani, Burmese and English as people exchanged news about mutual friends and told tales of the trek. We were all enormously relieved when the driver, turning his head round and lifting a corner of his scarf off his mouth, shouted out, 'Imphal!'

As we drove in, Imphal was very much alert. Refugees were streaming into the town and thronging around the evening bazaar, which was ablaze with little oil lamps and candles. As we tumbled out of the bus, camp helpers rushed backwards and forwards among the crowd. A confused babble of voices filled the air.

'Come on, let's try and get clear of the mob,' Lucy called out.

Gracie let out a groan. 'I feel all in. I could just lie down and die right here.'

'Not here, please,' Lucy said.

Kureeya was organising some boys to help with our luggage; I stopped with him and then followed him through the crowd and down the hill. I was relieved to be able to stretch my legs and was looking forward to settling into the camp and an evening meal.

Suddenly, there were terrifying shrieks and people were shouting. Kureeya pulled me sharply across the road, the luggage on his head cascading around. As I struggled to keep upright, the bus lumbered past us. I could see that there was no driver in the front, but some of the evacuees were still on board, holding on to each other and clinging to the seat backs. Almost immediately there was a tremendous bang as the bus veered over towards the wall and crashed into it, sliding forwards for fifteen yards or so before stopping.

There was an onslaught of noise and, above it all, the terrible sound of children screaming. People started rushing down to the bus, which was tilted over to one side. Kureeya ran towards the front of it. I picked up one or two of our bags as I followed him, hardly knowing what I was doing, scarcely believing. Then I saw Lucy and Julia emerging through the dusk from in front of the vehicle, where it was pinned against the wall. Thank God, I thought. Oh, thank God.

But then Julia ran up to me and grabbed hold of my arms tightly as if to hold herself up, her voice pitched high.

'Laura, we've lost Gracie. The bus missed us by inches. I thought she was right behind us but we can't see her.'

*

It took what seemed to be several hours to move the bus away from the wall, and all the while the shouts and cries shattered the night. Lanterns were brought and medical personnel from the field hospital arrived with stretchers and emergency equipment. They had to cut away bars at the windows, and Kureeya helped to get the injured passengers out. They found Gracie right by the front wheel, unconscious and hardly breathing, together with a dozen fatalities and badly injured. Lucy almost threw herself on her friend, and we had to hold her back. We followed the stretcher as they took her to the town's small hospital. I heard Lucy trying to tell them about Gracie's pregnancy, but she was gently moved away and we could do nothing but wait outside, unable to talk, hardly able to think.

*

Much later, the doctor came out to tell us that Gracie had died. We had seen where the bus had crushed her chest and shoulder, and her limp body as they carried her. But her face had remained untouched. We had been clinging to shreds of hope. Now we held each other, finally allowing the tears we'd been holding back.

Lucy and Julia wouldn't leave, wanting to stay near Gracie for the night. But I felt that I had to get away from everything – from the hospital, from the crowd and the chaos.

Julia hugged me and said, 'You go, Laura. Go and find somewhere you can sleep. Kureeya will help you.' Kureeya had stayed alongside us since Gracie had been carried in, still holding on to our bits of luggage – silent and with a dignity that he always had about him.

So I left them there and I went back with Kureeya towards the camp on the outskirts of the town, dazed and my legs weak. All the tiredness from the last few weeks seemed to have caught up with me. I felt breathless and my nerves were shattered. I suddenly realised I couldn't face the camp and asked Kureeya if he would walk with me.

We went without talking out of the town, crossed some fields and followed a path that led to a stony outcrop. We sat down, I with my arms round my knees, staring out at the darkness, Kureeya with his legs crossed, his feet tucked under him. Kureeya had torn his shirt and head cloth for bandages and was now bare-chested, a piece of cloth draped around his neck. Our shoulders brushed for a moment. It didn't seem to matter. None of it mattered.

'Memsahib?'

'Yes, Kureeya.' I turned towards him. His thick hair merged with the darkness behind. My head was throbbing and my eyelids felt heavy, but I could just see him looking at me, unblinking. I realised what it was about Kureeya. He never looked away.

'When you get to Calcutta, memsahib, you will have your husband. He will come. They are all coming now, even the army.'

'I know. What will you do?'

He was silent for a moment, rubbing his forehead. 'You British will not go back,' he said. 'India also will be free. That is our future.'

I said nothing for a few minutes and looked out into the darkness, almost wishing to be absorbed into the night. After a while, I pushed myself up and said, 'You must be cold. I certainly am. Let's go back.'

*

I lay down as I was on a bamboo cot that night alongside strangers, not knowing nor caring where my few possessions were. When I closed my eyes, Kureeya was sitting at the side of the cot, his shoulders wrapped in a bit of blanket. He had left before I woke up the next morning, with the light pricking my eyelids and heavy, disturbing dreams fading as the noise of the camp penetrated my consciousness. Lucy was crouching down on the tarpaulin next to me, calling my name.

'Laura, Kureeya told me where you were. Were you up all night? We stayed with Gracie and couldn't sleep anyway. What are we going to tell Bertha when she comes?'

Tears started in Lucy's eyes, and she rubbed at them with the palms of her hands. 'Bertha told me back in Tamu that Gracie's Tim is dead as well. She didn't want to say anything until Gracie was safely in Mussoorie.'

I thought of the day we first met up with Bertha. 'Do you think Gracie had some sort of suspicion?'

'Perhaps she did, because she hardly mentioned him after that first day.'

It seemed possible that Gracie had realised all along. I thought back to a change in her mood throughout the last part of the trek, although she kept up a cheerful enough front, as we all did. We found Julia, and I washed and cleaned myself up as best I could.

Gracie and her unborn baby were buried as the sun began to rise in the sky. I stood with the others, thinking of her beautiful eyes with their arching brows. As we made our way back into the camp we walked almost mechanically, side by side, none of us willing to break the silence.

*

Lucy and I waited for the buses from Palel. When Bertha, Vera and the boys climbed down from the bus, they waved to us wildly. I took Tommy and Ben to one side, and I could see Lucy, gripping Bertha's wrists and moving her head jerkily as she explained the accident and how Gracie had died. I told the boys as gently as I could about our arrival, about the bus and how we must all be terribly brave for Bertha, who was Gracie's cousin, and for Lucy and Julia, who were her friends.

Tommy listened, pale and silent. Then, a deep frown creasing his brow, he shouted, 'She's not dead. She's not. You're lying!' He burst out sobbing and Ben joined in. Vera rushed over to us and the boys clung to her.

We stayed in Imphal for the rest of the day and were put up in a tent in the corner of the compound of the *dak* bungalow, away from the camp itself. Kureeya made us tea on the lawn in a passable china tea service brought from the bungalow. He had bathed and someone had given him a clean shirt and shorts, and he had wound a head cloth once more around his head. As he squatted by the kerosene burner, I noticed how thin his long calves were and the deep cracks around the heels of his bare feet.

'Memsahib, *chai.*'

'Thank you.' I looked at him, but he was already moving away to the burner, half stooped, his back towards me.

*

Later on, there were visitors to our tent; some planters' wives who were helping out in the camp brought us food in *tiffin* carriers.

'What a terrible time you've had,' said a woman of nearly six foot in her early fifties, with thinning, silver-white hair, 'to leave your homes and your lives back there, and then to meet up with such a tragedy just as you were reaching safety.'

I felt a sudden longing, not for my own home, but for the Hut at Kokine, afternoon tea on the lawn with my cousins, the padouk tree in full bloom, Jo-Jo jumping on and off the bench which ran around its trunk. Thank goodness Aunt Louisa, Fran, Mouse and the girls would be waiting in Calcutta. At least the Family would pull through.

*

We left Imphal the next morning at seven-thirty. We had to cover nearly ninety miles to Kohima, the local Manipur state capital, and then another forty miles or so to Dimapur. The road was good and we raced first through dense forests, then across paddy fields, climbing in a steady ascent from the plains through ranges of hills, bamboo jungle and mist-covered pines – an ever-changing scene. There was a fresh, cool breeze as we left the stagnant air of the plains behind, and the boys distracted themselves with an imitation of the constant hooting of the horns. The traffic streamed one way only as we approached Mao Gate, a small township on the main highway. Lucy had hardly left Bertha's side since Bertha arrived in Imphal the previous morning and they now sat close together. If Bertha had been holding herself together for Gracie since we met up, she now looked defeated and drained. I couldn't bear to think about what she was coping with. Her husband missing, and now Gracie, and it seemed that Tim was dead as well.

We were all subdued as we continued to climb to the highest point, nearly six thousand feet up, to the local capital. The town sat astride the ridge and was lovely with a hundred varieties of trees, a riot of cultivated flowers, but I felt unmoved.

We had to wait at the top for several hours for the upward stream of traffic to stop before we could move again. We descended swiftly on a ledge cut out from the mountain rock and the magnificence of the scenery was at last soothing – the deep hues of the jungle and the afternoon sun flashing on the bend of the river. We finally left the mountain range through a narrow gorge, emerging into more gentle, dusty hills, surrounded by giant trees, serenaded by the guttural bellowing of bullfrogs.

Some fifteen miles from Dimapur, the road straightened out altogether and in the early evening the bus drew into the railway station. The station was dark and gloomy, lit by a couple of oil lamps, and the small platform was filled with a surging mass of people. We had been travelling all day, the bus making heavy work of the steep climbs and perilous bends. We were desperate for something to drink, but had to push through the crowds to get our permits and tickets to travel.

'Into the waiting room!' Vera screamed above the noise, hustling the boys along as they tried to follow me into the booking office, but it was impossible to move forward.

231

Bertha and Kureeya stood slightly apart from us, together with Lucy and Julia. Lucy had been silent since we left Imphal and I could pick her out now in the faint light, standing with her arms folded, square and small, almost hidden in the crowd. She lifted her hand up in a slight wave. Then it was a flurry of porters and baggage as we tried to push our way into the dining room.

*

We were back on the platform in good time for the train to arrive, anxious to secure our seats. Around us, people were calling out, balancing improbably high loads of bedrolls and suitcases and bundles on their heads. As the train edged into the station just before midnight, its smoke plume visible above the line of the dimly-lit platform, the crowd surged forward and I grabbed Tommy's hand.

Kureeya supervised as our few bits of luggage were loaded and helped the boys get on the train with Bertha and Vera. Julia fought her way on ahead of me and Lucy then pushed me up into the carriage. She climbed behind me, urged forward by the swell of evacuees on the platform. I swung out from the top step to look along the platform. I thought I could pick out Kureeya, his head cloth caked with the red Manipur dust, moving through the frantic, jostling crowds, then disappearing towards the third-class compartments.

19

BOBBY

March and April 1942

On 21 and 22 March the Japanese unleashed waves of bombing on Magwe, a heavy blow to our airforce. About a week or so later, at the end of March, I passed Lion on the road to Magwe. Ismail was driving the jeep, but I leaned across and hooted at my cousin, then got out and ran over to where he was standing by an old bus that was packed to the hilt with people and luggage. He was heading to Minbu where he had been posted – some more foolishness, he called it. I could tell that he was furious and thought it was all a big mistake, but he seemed now to be accepting whatever the authorities dished up, convinced that he could sort it out pretty quickly. Once he got to Magwe later that day, he came over to Telegraph headquarters. I was having tea with Simon, the sub-divisional officer in charge, and Lion joined us. The SDO was a talkative chap, and I could sense that my cousin was still indignant about his bus journey and was getting irritated. He was obviously exhausted as well and absolutely obsessed with getting a serviceable car and enough petrol to evacuate at short notice.

I was on the road again the following day and, to keep Lion happy, I agreed to bring his own jeep back from Mandalay. Ismail could drive it while I came back in my own Ford GP.

In Mandalay, I stayed in the house in Aungbale overnight. The place was stuffed full of mosquitoes, and the air in the house was stifling. As I had the afternoon free the following day, I drove the couple of hours up to Maymyo to see the Lamonts and spend Good Friday morning with them. In the evening, Lamont went off to his room early, taking a bottle of whisky with him. The room was dim, lit only by a covered lamp to maintain the blackout, and some candles. Eva started waltzing around the room, then pulled me up from my chair, singing in her light, contralto voice the song we'd played endlessly on the vacation in Kalaw when I first met her – what now seemed a lifetime ago.

> *'Stardust scattered all along the highway*
> *On a rainbow coloured skyway . . .'*

'I found you!' I boomed out, down in my boots, and we fell about laughing. 'No, seriously,' I said, then grinned, and we continued singing together, Eva's giggles turning her voice into quavers. Eva put a record on and wound up the gramophone.

'Come on, Bobby, let's be the best dancers in the world tonight. Astaire and Rogers, you'd better watch out. People will frown and say, "While Burma fell, they danced the night away!" Well, I don't care. Maybe they'll even make a motion picture out of us!'

'And will it be a great success?' I murmured into her hair. I suddenly found her closeness almost unbearable.

'Ah! That, you silly boy, you will have to wait for the premiere of the picture to find out.'

She pulled back and smiled at me, and then I drew her to me again and felt the tension suddenly leave her so that I almost had to hold her up. I had never known Eva not to chatter like a bird through any occasion. But that evening neither one of us said much. We danced until the town slept around us, swaying together slowly when the music stopped and until, one by one, the candles went out. Later, our hands linked, we moved over to the small sofa underneath the window and, whispering, I told her of the excitement and terror of being on the road, and we talked about the holiday in Kalaw when we first met. I could see the barest outline of Eva's face in the patches of moonlight seeping into the room through the blackout, the small, slightly dimpled chin tilted upwards towards me, the wisps of her hair at the temples, almost silvery in the thin light. Early in the morning I kissed her softly, questioning, then deeply, gripping the top of her arms. Eva was weeping silently, her tears running down her cheeks, which she rubbed against my eyes and my mouth.

'Don't talk, don't say anything. Darling Bobby!' she murmured.

*

The next morning was Good Friday. It was the day that Mandalay was bombed, leaving the town a scene of utter destruction and I drove back down from Maymyo without waiting for orders. The town was an obvious target. Fort Dufferin in the centre of Mandalay was one of the main military supply depots. But I don't suppose anyone was quite prepared for the town's wholesale devastation. The telegraph office was damaged by the bombing, cutting off all communications, and we had an urgent job to get a telegraphic link back up. Fortunately, the telegraph girls were lucky to escape the hit and were able to get back to their jobs, as Mandalay was central to our communications with the administration in Maymyo and the war zone.

That day, I drove into the Fort in the blistering heat, skirting round craters of unexploded bombs. I saw Chinese soldiers, newly arrived in Mandalay as part of the defence against the Japanese advance; they were bathing in the moat – a strange sight. Inside the Fort, large sections of the Sappers' and Miners' barracks had disappeared, although there was hardly any other damage.

The railway station had been destroyed, and I was told that fierce flames had devoured at least half of the town in a matter of a few hours. What made it worse was that the fire brigade had been wiped out with a direct hit, so there was no firefighting force. Fires were raging and, at first, it seemed to me that the whole town was gutted. It was a complete mess, with bodies and charred dead cattle still lying at the side of the road. Trees were burnt down and nearly the whole of the area south of B Road was burnt out. The Sessions Court and other government buildings were intact but a fire was burning around the general hospital and the cathedral.

*

Throughout April things became more and more chaotic. As the Japanese advanced north of Toungoo, you could sense

235

that everyone was getting ready for a full retreat. All means of transport were being rounded up by the authorities to provide for the army should they need to go, so that made it increasingly difficult for the civilian population to make their way out. It wasn't surprising that people were panicking, particularly after Mandalay was bombed, when large numbers of refugees were burnt in the overcrowded camps in which they had been held. I was up and down the main road from Mandalay, part of a constant stream of army vehicles and lorries carrying stores, ammunition and troops. As the army retreated, we destroyed the communications behind us and I continued to move along the line of the Japanese advance, checking that forward communications were open, as well as bringing up the personnel from the abandoned areas.

I caught up with my father and Lion in Mandalay a few days after the bombing, and found Harry with them. They were still in the Aungbale Street house, which was in a dreadful condition. There was no electricity and the household was reduced to minimal rations, as the bazaar and shops were closed. Mandalay itself was just a shell, fires still burning and with a smell of unburied bodies everywhere. There were few people about; instead the town now seemed to be mainly populated by stray dogs.

The atmosphere between my father and cousin was barely civil and, perhaps for the first time, I was glad to have Harry there. He told me about his journey with Laura as far as Mawlaik in February and the stories that he'd heard about the sickness on the route out to Palel and the constant threat from *dacoits*. He said he was finally able to sleep properly now that Laura was safely in Calcutta with Aunt Louisa and the others.

Lion was on a constant errand to get petrol. He was going back to Maymyo and I gave him a note for Eva. With the telegraph lines down, I was myself back in Maymyo about a week later, but had only an hour to spare. There was no one in at the Lamonts', so I went round to my aunt Bea's. She was alone with the servant as Lester was out. Issie's baby had been born in early March. She had a dreadful time getting away and had only recently been evacuated with the baby by air through Shwebo, just north of Mandalay, with her priority status for women with children – and just in time before the airfield closed.

Maymyo was suffering almost constant early morning bombing raids. The Japanese were now close and there was often no warning for people to leave their beds and get to the trenches in the jungle.

I knew that Bea was having a difficult time. She was in bed when I arrived, and I was shocked to find out that she'd suffered a mild heart attack a few days before.

'Don't worry, darling,' she said. 'Lester is looking after me and Lion's been in Maymyo for the last few days, so he's been in and out of the house.'

'You should be getting out through Shwebo while the route's still open, Auntie.'

'Lester is in the same boat as Lion, Bobby. They won't give him his leave papers. And now, you see, I'm not really fit to travel, am I? So I shall just wait for Lester and we'll go together.'

I noticed the rosary on the little table at the side of the bed.

'It's the air raids that are getting us all down, Bobby. I was so pleased when Issie left with the baby. It's very unsettling; not a single night without having to leave our beds. I just don't want to have to do it anymore. We will have to pray, that's all.' She sighed and turned her head away slightly.

*

On 15 April I was sent down to Minbu, a small town just north of Magwe, to bring up their telegraph people. The sun was blazing by mid-morning and the air was stifling. It was really a ghost town as most of the civilians had left already, but they were still waiting for orders for official evacuation. It seemed that the following day the Additional Deputy Commissioner discussed matters with the Brigadier and was satisfied that there was nothing further that the civil authorities could do for the army, and he handed over to the Brigadier a small party of army signallers from the corps at Magwe; they had apparently been forgotten about and were in danger of being left at Minbu. The Additional DC spent a good deal of the day going round the power station, the water pumping station and other installations which were due to be demolished; it seems he himself personally blew up the Irrigation Department telephone exchange as his final act before leaving Minbu that evening.

I was back in Maymyo the following day and went straight to Aunt Bea's. Lion was there. Both he and Lester finally had their papers and Lion was leaving the following day – to walk out, heading for the Tamu route. Lion and my father had quarrelled badly the week before, with the result that Lion had received a letter from my father saying that he was leaving for India independently. But no one knew where he was. I was hurt that he hadn't sent word to me and I was worried, not wanting to think of him setting out alone. In fact, I felt angry with Lion for falling out with him at such a time.

Lion had been carrying about a note for me from Eva. The writing was uncertain and shaky.

Maymyo, 12 April 1942

My sweet old thing,
I don't know how I missed you when you were here. DON'T DO IT AGAIN!! I hope your dreadful cousin manages to get this through to you.

Everything here is in chaos since the bombing. People are really nervous now that Shwebo is shut off. We should leave. What do you think?

Love, Eva.
PS You are the only sane thing around here.

With the Shwebo airfield closed, Aunt Bea and Uncle Lester were going to try to leave by air through Myitkyina, as my aunt wasn't fit for the overland route. They weren't guaranteed any priority and the only thing for them to do was to get to Myitkyina itself, over three hundred miles further north, and wait there. They would be joining the thousands of refugees who were making their way north in whatever way they could. Everyone knew that this was the last chance to get out by air and the evacuation had become a mad scramble. They were leaving their dog Juno with the cook and my aunt was putting a brave face on it. 'The poor darling,' she said. 'She won't understand, will she?'

I collected them in the jeep well before dawn the following morning. Aunt Bea was in a state of near collapse when I arrived.

'Bobby, we're going to have to leave nearly everything here. We are only allowed about thirty pounds of luggage each, you know.'

I gathered up her bags. 'Auntie, don't even think about it. We have to let it all go. Let's just be grateful that you're getting out.'

'Do you have any news of Robert?'

'No, but he can look after himself. Who knows, he may have left the country already and wasn't able to let us know. Please don't worry about anything – just yourselves.'

We drove all day, arriving in the early evening. The road to the airfield was crowded with dishevelled and dirty-looking refugees. Once there, we could see long rows of injured soldiers lying in the open field on the dry, burnt grass. The Survey School had been turned into a huge camp and there were hundreds of people sitting on the floor on boxes, lying on bedrolls and tables or restlessly milling around.

I had to leave Bea and Lester there, with their few bits of luggage around them, not knowing if they would make it. For all the privileges we tried to hang on to, I thought, war and disasters had an effect of levelling people out. They looked small, insignificant, indistinguishable from the rest of the evacuees, despite the freshness of their clothes.

*

I was ordered back to Mandalay and was as keen as ever to get back to the Lamonts in Maymyo. Eva had said nothing to indicate her state of mind in her note, but I sensed that she was becoming desperate. In the previous week the town had suffered badly from bombing raids and was in a dreadful condition, the roads pitted by craters. Many of the government departments had evacuated out of Maymyo to Myitkyina, and people were being urged to leave the town and move to Mandalay, ready for evacuation.

Luckily, I found Eva at home. She was pleased to see me, but she looked exhausted, was distracted and often close to tears.

'I don't think we'll see Mummy again. Pops hardly ever talks about her now. He feels guilty about leaving her in Rangoon and I think he's forgotten how hard we both tried to make her move, to make her come with us, but she just wouldn't. What could he have done?'

We came near to quarrelling. Eva said, 'You could just drive us out straightaway. By all accounts the troops are pulling out any day now. Do you think the army bigwigs will care what happens to you when the time comes? You will see, they will be the first to clear out on the road they've kept safely for themselves, and we are the ones that will all be left behind for the Japs.'

'That's foolish talk. What are you saying, Eva? I can't listen to it. You know I can't.' I was suddenly angry with her and I didn't quite understand why. We both fell silent. Then I said, 'Let's see what my orders are when I get back again. I'll be here again in one or two days. But try to go now if you can. Can't you join up with some of the others who are leaving? You must have the contacts in the camp, and with your persuasiveness . . .'

Eva looked away without responding. There was a distance between us I didn't understand.

I added, 'Of course I'll do what I can, but I've got to push off now. If you haven't gone when I get back, maybe I can help you out somehow.'

*

I drove down the main road to Mandalay, littered with abandoned vehicles. Conditions in the town were appalling. Since the end of March, the city had been swept by smallpox and cholera. It seemed that the cholera epidemic alone was claiming over five hundred victims a day. It was the refugees that suffered most, trapped in the overcrowded, insanitary camps. Towards the end of April, as the remaining troops and the last ditchers left Mandalay, the administration started to clear the refugee camps, transferring the evacuees in lorries to transit camps along the Chindwin river.

Many of the telegraph girls, who were very largely Anglo-Indian and Anglo-Burmese, had their families in a small camp in the central part of Mandalay, close by the telegraph offices. They didn't have any priority status for evacuation, but I was given authorisation to help them evacuate by joining the convoys heading north. Ismail and I spent a couple of days ferrying the families up to the convoys. They were moving slowly enough, Canadian Chevrolet trucks – the CMPs – with their huge tyres and high fronts, like lumbering beasts. They had specially-trained Indian drivers and it was easy enough to get one of the drivers to stop and take the families on board. But it was getting too late for many of the evacuees I passed on the road, groups of twenty or so together, or sometimes as many as a hundred. The villages were full to overflowing and food was scarce. For many of them it seemed safer to stay where they were in the camps, waiting for God knows who to get them out, than to leave and risk the danger of attack from the Japanese or from the vagabond bands who were roaming the countryside.

It was nearly one week before I could return to Maymyo. The town was almost empty, with the last evacuees waiting to be taken down to Mandalay that night. I had convinced myself that Eva would have left. Arriving in the early evening, I found the Lamonts' bungalow in darkness. I called out as I went up the steps, and a thin beam of light shone out from the veranda, casting shadows against the front of the house; Paul Lamont eased himself out of a cane chair that had been hidden by the overhanging laburnum. Even in the dim torchlight I could see that his hair was uncombed and his clothes looked unkempt. He must be losing his grip entirely, I thought. Before I could ask about Eva, Lamont caught hold of my sleeve and brought his unshaven face close to mine.

'My dear boy, I have shocking news. Eva, you see. They didn't have any vaccinations, but she didn't tell me. She must have been exhausted and couldn't fight it off; I should have seen what was happening to her. It was cholera, Bobby.' He took out a large handkerchief from the pocket of his crumpled jacket and blew his nose. 'Eva died. What can I say to you, Bobby, I know how fond you were of her. How will her mother take it?' He looked at me with watering eyes while I struggled to grasp what he was saying.

They shouldn't even have been there still. Why hadn't they left? My head seemed to be exploding.

'Wait for me here. I'll be back.'

I threw myself down the steps and through the front gate. The shock was so intense that I felt winded, and an acute pain ran across my shoulders and back. I hadn't even considered the possibility that something would happen to Eva. I had to keep moving while my head ran wild. I should have convinced her to stop her work in the camps. She had never been strong enough. Why hadn't I asked her whether she had been vaccinated? Why hadn't the authorities checked? She had been right: it was every damn man for his own damn self.

'NO!' I shouted, and I could feel the tears block the top of my nose and pound against my eyelids.

I walked out to the club and round the golf course, through to the edge of the jungle beyond Government House, unconcerned by the curfew and impervious to the sense of menace that hung about the town. Only a few months earlier the track had been one of the popular horse rides and a good spot for hunting small deer, jungle fowl and partridge. It was almost completely dark by this time, the sky a deep blue, the night encroaching in black streaks. The incessant high-pitched noise of the cicadas joined with the noisy throb in my head. Eva was a softly-pleading ghost that accompanied me as I strode behind the town. But some time that night I banished her in my anger, so when I finally went back to the bungalow I was calm and my mind was made up. Paul Lamont was asleep in a chair, a light cover pulled up over him.

'Take what you need, Paul. We're going and I'm getting you out of Burma before the Japs bomb the Ava Bridge.'

I didn't have the heart to go into Eva's bedroom. I was carrying a creased snap of her in my breast pocket, taken among the pines in Kalaw, and I put my hand up to it as I went out into the small compound, lighting up a cigarette. I had developed an open sore on the side of my foot, which was starting to swell. Lamont shuffled around the bungalow silently with a torch, collecting a few books, all that he was taking with him from a lifetime in Burma. He hadn't mentioned Daw Min Min.

For the last time, we headed down, round the hairpin bends to the ruins that were Mandalay. The town was utterly desolate, with the stench of death hanging over everything. Ismail and I scoured the pounds until we found a truck we could exchange for the GP. I found that my orders were to evacuate a group of telegraph girls who were still in the city. It was just what I'd hoped for and in the early hours of the following day, with Lamont, the girls and their luggage in the back, Ismail and I joined a convoy of army lorries and other transport. We headed south-west to Ava, once the capital of Burma, and over the massive new cantilever bridge across the Irrawaddy. I had made up my mind I was finished with Burma and I carried straight on to Tamu, where I sent off a signal saying that I was proceeding with the evacuation to India and that there would be no need for me to come back again.

At Tamu I went to the depot and picked up another truck, a brand new Canadian Chevrolet, and ran straight down to Dimapur in a day and a half, snatching some sleep by the side of the road. The road from Tamu was freshly constructed and not fully tarmacked – a steady descent along the edge of cliffs. We were silent, the girls terrified of the treacherous road, Paul Lamont locked into his own internal misery. My foot was festering and had been dressed in the camp, my shoe cut to take the bandage. Ismail had taken over the driving at Tamu and he was hidden behind his tightly-wound scarf, his eyes alone showing, fixed on the road ahead. Just outside Tamu, I looked behind at the steady convoy of vehicles and across at the blue-edged hills, and bade a bitter farewell to Burma, not knowing at what point precisely we crossed the border.

20

CHRISSIE

June 1986

My father leaned forward slightly in his chair, blowing his lips out gently in a barely audible sound.

'So, you see, Chrissie, I was out of Burma in the end before Lion and Daddy.' He seemed relieved to reach the end of his story. 'As you know, my father did get out quite safely. In fact, he trekked out together with Lion in the end, and we all met up in Calcutta sometime in May. They were lucky because Imphal was badly bombed a couple of days after they went through and a lot of the evacuees were killed. It was only just in time for us all because, right at the end of April, only a day or so after I left with the girls for Tamu, the Japanese opened fire on Monywa with all they had, machine guns and mortars. Trucks, jeeps and every other kind of vehicle were given orders to dump everything they were carrying and load up with army personnel, together with the sick and wounded, and take off. So I left at the right time, didn't I? Our own troops blew the Ava Bridge a day or so after I left, to prevent the Japanese from advancing further. The Governor himself flew out to India from Myitkyina a few days later before the airfield closed. So he was all right. And then Stilwell also – the Allied Commander – he had to trek out with his staff. If I hadn't got out when I did, I might never have made it . . .'

I waited. The warmth and calm of the Hertfordshire summer flowed in through the open window.

'Of course there were thousands who didn't get out. No one ever knew the numbers of those who didn't make it, but it was hundreds of thousands left behind. And those that trekked out in time, so many of them died on the way, caught up in the monsoon. The ones who came the way we did were the lucky ones, but those trapped up in the north had to make it up the

Hukawng Valley and into Assam that way. Terrible country. And in the monsoon pretty well impassable. We all knew people we never saw again.'

'What happened to Bea and Lester?' Until my father told me his story, I had never heard of my grandmother's sister and her husband.

'We didn't ever hear what happened to Aunt Bea or Lester – whether they got out of Burma. They *must* have done, because I took them myself to Myitkyina. But there weren't many planes leaving by then, and then the flights stopped completely. And the Japanese were close, you know. We didn't see them up in Mussoorie, which is where the Family went when we all collected in India, and we didn't ever see them again.'

'Do you think they never got on a flight out?'

My father shook his head and looked down. He fumbled for a while with his handkerchief and then blew his nose.

'I don't like to think of those times, Chrissie. And then Daddy died soon after we got to India. A lot of the older ones did, after they had survived the trek. It was too much for them . . . Of course, we'd lost our homes, everything.'

'Were you there when he died?'

'No, I wasn't, and I never really got over it. I decided to go back to Burma, and they were sending me for training with the élite corps – Colonel Wingate's men. The plan was that we should be parachuted back into the country to infiltrate enemy lines. So I went to say goodbye to the Family. When I left, Daddy shook my hand and said, "You're going to do all right, son." That meant an awful lot to me, but it was the last time that I saw him. A few weeks later I had a telegram saying that he had died . . . It was a terrible time.'

'And what happened to Harry after the trek?' I asked after supper. 'I always knew that Laura had been married at one time, but I've never heard anything about her husband. Did she leave him? Or what happened?'

'Yes, she did. Harry got out, I know that, because they all met up in Calcutta. But Laura never lived with him in India and I don't know what happened to him later on. Of course, it caused a terrible fuss with the Family because they didn't want anything to do with divorce in those days. After Daddy died, Aunt Louisa replaced him as the head of the household. They both had very firm views on these things.'

My father told me about the time when Laura lost her babies and how the Family never talked about it. But he knew that her one lasting regret after her divorce was that she had no children, and at times her unhappiness about it had become almost an obsession.

While my father was fixing a last pot of tea before my drive home, I thought about Laura and her brief marriage to Harry, and how in the end she left everything she knew behind her. After her trek through the mountains into India and in the years that followed, she made decisions that changed her life. I wondered whether, during the empty evenings in south London, she was haunted by memories of the lakes at Kokine, the summers in Kalaw and the friends and family who had been lost in that scramble from Burma in 1942. Or perhaps her other life had faded like the prints of pagodas and the Irrawaddy that hung in the sitting room. I wondered if Laura and the others finally closed a door behind them after Lion died and they lost his pension – forced into selling his precious books and the jewellery sent out from Burma after the first bombings; until in the end they only had old tobacco tins of gemstones that were taken up to London, one by one, to be sold to meet their bills.

But then I thought about the trek and the women who had shared with Laura a long walk into an uncertain future. She must have remembered Bertha, and wondered if she'd met up with her husband – whether he'd survived the war in a Japanese prison camp; wondered about Julia and Lucy, and if they'd ever gone back home to Burma; and about Gracie, who had never reached safety. Surely Laura must have always carried with her the imprint of those times.

When my father came back with the tea, I asked, 'What about Lion?' I had a faint recollection of him in the early 1960s, shortly before he died, emerging from his study to drink a whisky soda with us, wearing a black linen jacket and shapeless trousers, with some sort of skull cap on his head.

'Lion returned to Rangoon in 1945 to work with the government. By then the Burmese nationalists, who had fought with the Japanese to kick the British out, changed tack and joined up with the Allied troops to help us defeat the Japanese. Only the men went back, just to tie things up, you know. When Lion got there, the Hut at Kokine was still standing, but it was in a terrible state; it had been used by the Japanese Army for something or other. Of course, he'd been great pals with some of the top people in the country before the war and he had kept up with the administration in exile in India. But Burma was heading for independence by then and those old politicians and civil servants were discredited . . . because they'd worked for the British, you see.'

My father was silent for a moment. When he started again, his voice dropped.

'We wanted to do what we could, but there was no place for us in Burma after the war. The Family left India for London in the middle of 1947 and Lion joined them all soon afterwards, just before the country became independent. I don't know . . . He didn't ever seem quite right after he left Burma. It had taken the heart right out of him. He never really found a job, just did bits of writing, gave talks – that sort of thing. I suppose he was too old to start again. He buried himself in his books and met some of the old crowd at reunions every now and then. And he always drank rather a lot, which was a dreadful pity. Of course, it was a terrible blow, leaving our home like that. You see, Lion really loved Burma. What did he say in the poem you found? *Burma laid a spell on me.* That's what it was, darling – a spell. You could never be rid of it.'

GLOSSARY

Ayah	Nursemaid or nanny
Bawmbie(s)	Shan pyjama-like garment
Beedi	Thin cigarette filled with tobacco flakes and wrapped in leaf
Betel	Vine leaf with stimulant qualities, chewed in South and South-East Asia
Buffaloes	The RAF's 67 (Fighter) Squadron had sixteen Buffalo aircraft in Burma in 1942. They were supported by one squadron of AVG (American Volunteer Group), who flew Tomahawk P-40s.
Chaiwallah	Tea seller
Chapati	Flat bread made of wheat
Chaprasi	Messenger or orderly
Cheroot	Small cigar made with chopped tobacco leaves
Chinthe	A lion-like creature that is often seen at the entrance of pagodas and temples in Burma and elsewhere in South-East Asia
Chota peg	Drink of spirits, usually taken in the early evening
Chowkidar	Night watchman
Chulia	Indian merchant
Coolie	An unskilled labourer or porter from India or from some other Asian countries, usually hired for low or subsistence wages
'D' notice	Final notice of demolition following evacuation
Dacoit	Bandit, robber
Dah	Flat knife
Dak bungalow	Government bungalow put up for travellers
Dhoolie	Sling-type litter, usually slung by a frame or poles
Dhoti	Loose cloth worn by men around the lower part of the body
'E' notice	Evacuation notice indicating only 'essential' inhabitants to remain
Gaung baung	Traditional head covering worn by Burmese men

Gharry	Horse-drawn cab or carriage
Ghee	Clarified butter
Godown	Warehouse
Hti	Conical structure, or umbrella, at the top of a stupa or a pagoda
Jaldi	Hurry *(Hindustani)*
Lascar	A seaman, often from South or South-East Asia
Longyi	Long cloth tucked into the waist, worn by Burmese men and women
Mahseer	Hindi name for a type of fish much favoured for angling in British India
Mali	An Indian gardener *(Hindustani)*
Manau	Traditional dance ceremony
Moiré	Silk fabric with rippled finish
Nat	Spirit
Nimbu	Lime *(Hindustani)*
Pah	Basket
Pi-dog, pariah dog	Dog without owner, found in the villages and towns
Poongyi	Buddhist priest
Sampan	Flat-bottomed wooden boat
Serang	Burmese boatman, in charge of the crew
Sola topee	Pith helmet, worn to protect against the sun
Stupa	Buddhist structure in South-East Asia and India, built in a variety of forms
Tamasha	Indian festival, entertainment or theatre
Thanaka	Cosmetic paste made from bark
Thakin	Master; the Thakin movement, Burmese movement for independence in 1930s, led by radical students
Thajee	Burmese village headman
Tiffin	A light meal

ACKNOWLEDGEMENTS

This book was inspired by the experience of my family in Burma after the bombing of Rangoon in December 1941, and their separate evacuation stories, particularly those of Andrew Hazlewood, Laurie Hazlewood, Leo (Pab) Robertson and Molly Greenaway. I am indebted to Pab for his diary and for his poem 'Burma', and to the wider family for their legacy.

My father, Bill Ellis, passed on to me his love of social history and believed in this book from the start. My aunt, Hazel Walker, shared her memories of Kokine, read an early draft and gave her blessing and encouragement. My son, Daniel Ellis, never lost faith.

I am enormously grateful to those who read the manuscript and offered encouraging comments and helpful suggestions: Vivienne Barton, Libby Cooper, Kate Ellis, Mark Ellis, Felicity Goodall, Moira Lazarus, Kyi Kyi May and Jennie Milnes. Thanks also to the Outwriters group for their support and enthusiasm.

My thanks to the British Library for access to the India Office Records. The official files, diaries and other contemporary accounts were essential for my broader understanding of the details of the evacuation. Personal accounts in particular served to emphasise how other families might be able to trace their own history in the particular details of my family's story.

I referred to a number of published works, including: Aung San Suu Kyi, *Freedom from Fear*; Thant Myint-U, *The River of Lost Footsteps*; Major CM Enriquez, *Burma Invaded: 1942*; Felicity Goodall, *Exodus Burma: The British Escape through the Jungles of Death 1942*; Michael D. Leigh, *The Evacuation of Civilians from Burma*; Yvonne Vaz Ezdani, *Songs of the Survivors*; James Lunt, *A Hell of a Licking: The Retreat from Burma 1941-42*; Theippan Maung Wa, *Wartime in Burma*; Geoffrey Tyson, *Forgotten Frontier*; *and* Maurice Maybury, *Heaven-Born in Burma: Flight of the Heaven-born*.

I have quoted from the following poems and songs: *There's a Long, Long Trail A-winding,* by Stoddard King; *Boots,* by Rudyard Kipling; *Homeless Bird,* by Rabindranath Tagore; and *Santa Fé Trail,* by James Grafton Rogers. I have also referenced *Roll out the Barrel,* by Lew Brown and *We're Going to Hang Out the Washing on the Siegfried Line,* by Jimmy Kennedy.

I am most grateful to Grahame Nicholls for providing the cover photograph and to Susanna Kendall for drawing the three maps.

A particular thank you is due to Stephen Chalke and Susanna Kendall of Charlcombe Books for their skill and help in taking this project forward.